D1596413

An Introduction to Heathland Ecology

C. H. Gimingham

Professor of Botany
University of Aberdeen

Oliver & Boyd · Edinburgh

In the same series:
Mills: An Introduction to Freshwater Ecology
Cousens: An Introduction to Woodland Ecology

Related texts:
FitzPatrick: An Introduction to Soil Science
Tivy: Biogeography: A Study of Plants in the Ecosphere.

OLIVER & BOYD
Croythorn House
23 Ravelston Terrace
Edinburgh EH4 3TJ

A Division of Longman Group Limited

ISBN 0 05 0027743

Printed in Great Britain by
T. & A. Constable Ltd., Edinburgh

Contents

QH541
.5
.M6
.G56

Acknowledgements

This book draws on the work and achievements of many friends and colleagues, too numerous to mention individually. To all of them the author's thanks are extended. In particular, grateful acknowledgement is made to the following: Dr J. B. Kenworthy, for contributing the Appendix, Figs. 5.6, 6.2, 7.2, A.1 and Plate 4a; Mr B. J. F. Miller, for the instructions on trapping heathland invertebrates (Chapter 5, p. 72, no. 2), and for information on invertebrates used in Chapters 4 and 5: Mr N. Picozzi, for Figs. 1.1, 4.2, 4.4, 5.3 and 5.4; Dr E. A. FitzPatrick, for Fig. 2.5; Dr G. R. Miller for Fig. 5.5 and for Plates 1a and 1b; Mr E. Middleton, for preparing many of the black and white photographs for reproduction and for Figs. 3.3, 3.4, 3.8 and 3.9; Mr I. Moir, for Figs. 3.5 and 3.7; the authors named in the Figure captions for permission to reproduce diagrams, and the Publishers of the following Journals: Journal of Ecology (Figs. 3.2 and 8.1); Transactions of the Botanical Society of Edinburgh (Fig. 2.6); Journal of Biological Education (Fig. 5.9b); the Editor of 'Animal populations in relation to their food resources' and Blackwell Scientific Publications Ltd. for Figs. 6.3 and 6.5; Messrs Chapman & Hall Ltd. for Figs. 2.2, 5.1, 6.2, 6.4, 7.2 and Table 6 from C. H. Gimingham: *Ecology of Heathlands*. Invaluable contributions to the preparation of diagrams were made by Mrs L. Forbes and by Mr D. R. Paterson, who also helped in proof checking. Parts of the manuscript were typed by Mrs H. Murray and Miss P. A. Grinsted, whose skilled assistance is greatly appreciated.

Notes

Though many of the examples in this book are drawn from Scottish heaths, this should not reduce the usefulness of the book in other regions, for the principles apply throughout and more appropriate examples can readily be substituted. Common English names for plants and animals are used for those unfamiliar with the scientific names, but the latter are given at the first mention of all plants and some invertebrate animal groups to avoid confusion which may arise from variations in the use of English names.

Aberdeen, 1974   C. H. Gimingham

1 Introduction

In recent years many people have become familiar with the word 'ecology'. It crops up frequently in television programmes, in newspapers and in science fiction. Unfortunately this does not always mean that it is properly understood. There is probably a general acceptance that it has something to do with the environment, and many people would link it with the problems of pollution. To others it conveys an impression of enthusiasm for wildlife, and all that goes with the idea of conservation.

While ecology may from time to time include all these aspects, it should not be equated with any of them – for it amounts to a good deal more. It is one of the major approaches to biological science – that approach which is concerned with the interactions between living things and all the many components of their environment, and their interactions amongst themselves – the ways, for example, in which they become arranged in populations and communities. Certainly it has something to say in connection with the management of the natural environment, pollution control, wildlife conservation and many other contemporary problems, but the important point is that its advice on these matters is the outcome of intensive scientific investigation.

This immediately draws attention to the enormous width of the subject. It would be quite impossible to survey the whole of it in a short time. So the best way to gain an effective introduction to the scope of ecology is to select one particular example of a community of living things and examine it very thoroughly, considering not only the plants and animals concerned but also their non-living surroundings – the physics and chemistry of the environment. This involves not just a list of the organisms and description of their adaptations, but examination as well of all the biological processes taking place.

What is more, this kind of study can reveal the effects of man on populations or communities of plants and animals, and the habitats in which they live. It can lead to the establishment of principles upon which sound methods of land management should be based.

Agriculture, forestry, landscape architecture and nature conservation are all examples of land management to which ecological principles apply. In some cases, man is setting up more or less artificial systems, such as crops or plantations, so as to obtain a desired product; but in others he is concerned chiefly with maintaining or adjusting types of biological community which already exist. If his activities are to succeed in the long run, it is vital to be aware of and to understand the processes involved and for this reason detailed investigation is needed.

Heathlands offer unrivalled opportunities for this type of investigation. In the first place, they are relatively widespread throughout much of Britain (as well as other countries in W. Europe – pp.7–8), and so it is often easy to find good examples either for regular day-visits or for short intensive periods of fieldwork based on field centres.

Secondly, except among mountains and sand dunes, heath landscapes are to a great extent man-made and their vegetation is managed by man. So there is scope here for enquiry into the ecological impact of man, of his domestic grazing animals, and of fire – his chief management tool. At the same time, the plant and animal communities are composed of naturally-occuring, not cultivated, species. Because of this, investigations of the processes are not subject to extra complications introduced by the fundamental alterations to the habitat which go along with intensive agriculture.

A third point is that in understanding heathland communities almost every aspect of ecological theory and technique is involved in various instructive ways. For example, among the topics which must be included are the effects of climate and soil on the plant communities, competition between species, community dynamics, cyclical change, the development of pattern, production processes, energy flow, nutrient and water balance – all these are concerned in building up the complete picture. In addition, the great importance in heath vegetation of one particular plant – heather (*Calluna vulgaris*) – draws attention to dominance as a feature of certain kinds of plant community.

It is also an advantage that there is a substantial foundation of research on the origins and functioning of heathland communities, to serve as a background for the type of studies this book may suggest. By way of a bonus, the plants and animals of heath are attractive and interesting, yet not so diverse as to be overwhelming, while studies of heathlands are also of practical value in relation to the rival claims of a variety of different forms of land use. In Scotland and in the upland parts of England and Wales, heath (or moorland, which is perhaps the commoner term in these regions) is still used for sheep grazing and for the sport of grouse shooting, just as it has been for many years (p. 16). As a result, in spite of increasing acreages devoted to forestry and improved pasture, there are still wide expanses of heathland, whereas in the south of England and in neighbouring W. European countries, it is rapidly giving way to arable land or forestry plantations.

The relative merits of these various sorts of land use, and of conservation for amenity, recreation and wild-life protection must be decided not only on economic and social grounds, but also on the basis of sound ecological information on the long-term effects of the various types of land use and management. The results of any well-planned studies of heathlands will provide a welcome addition to the knowledge on which countryside planning must depend in the future.

Fig. 1.1. Heathland landscape in N.E. Scotland. A cultivated valley with heather-covered hills beyond, managed for sheep and grouse. The pattern of light and dark patches in the middle distance is the result of burning small strips and patches. (Photo: N. Picozzi.)

2 Heathland –
a problem of origins

Before starting to investigate the way a heath community functions it is necessary to build up as much background information as possible. One of the objectives will be to reach at least a partial explanation for the occurrence of heaths in the localities where we find them today. This involves on the one hand considering local examples in relation to the complete range of habitats occupied by heaths in Britain and Europe. On the other, it involves delving into history, turning up old records, finding antique maps, and getting hold of any available evidence on the past use and management of the area. This chapter provides some basic information against which to evaluate such a study.

What is a heath ?

It is not difficult to recognise a heath, but heathland means different things to different people. The same area may seem like a monotonous barren land to one observer, while another sees in it a fine view of open country, rich in colour especially in the late summer when the heather is in bloom (Plate 1a). Undoubtedly there is something highly characteristic about heath as a type of vegetation, but for ecological purposes we need a rather more precise description than can be found in a dictionary. What then are the main ecological characteristics of heathland vegetation?

The first is a negative characteristic – although none the less important. Trees are absent (or very sparse) on heaths (Fig. 1.1 and Plate 1b). Even tall bushes or shrubs are either absent or scarce but sometimes there may be patches of whin (or gorse, *Ulex europaeus*) or scattered bushes of juniper (*Juniperus communis* – Fig. 2.1).

Secondly, the main positive characteristic is the almost continuous cover of heather (Figs. 1.1, 2.1, 2.3, 2.7, and Plate 1) or one of its close relatives. Botanically, these can be described as dwarf-shrubs, many of them evergreen with very small leaves (Figs. 3.3, 3.4) – they are like a miniature forest of low, much-branched woody bushes forming a canopy which seldom stands more than about $\frac{1}{2}-\frac{3}{4}$ m high (Figs. 2.2, 2.3).

These dwarf-shrubs provide the dominant layer or 'stratum', below which there may be a variety of other plants – other dwarf-shrubs of a more creeping or straggling habit, some species of grasses, sedges, ferns, club-mosses, etc., and a ground stratum of mosses or lichens (Fig. 2.2). The extent to which these subordinate strata are developed depends on the habitat, and on the density of the uppermost stratum.

The last three paragraphs have provided a description of what is known as the 'physiognomy' of heath vegetation – that is, its general appearance and structure. They represent the main features constituting a 'formation group' – which is a type of vegetation recognisable wherever it may occur, in whatever part of the world, irrespective of the precise identity of the plant species composing the various communities.

Fig. 2.1. Heathland in N. Germany (Lüneburg heath). Heather with grasses and scattered bushes of juniper.

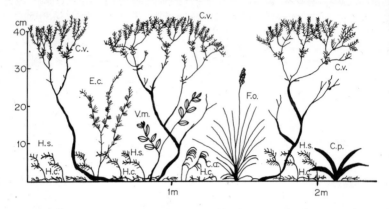

Fig. 2.2. Diagram of a section or profile through a heath community (heather with bell heather and blaeberry, N.E. Scotland). C.a. – *Cladonia arbuscula* (lichen); C.p. – *Carex pilulifera* (pill-headed sedge); C.v. – *Calluna vulgaris* (heather); E.c. – *Erica cinerea* (bell heather); F.o. – *Festuca ovina* (sheep's fescue); H.c. – *Hypnum cupressiforme* (moss); H.s. – *Hylocomium splendens* (moss); V.m. – *Vaccinium myrtillus* (blaeberry) (After Gimingham 1972).

Any example of vegetation which shows these general character-istics can be called heath, whether it comes from Britain, southern Sweden, western France, Canada, the Falkland Islands, or high up in the mountains of Africa or New Guinea. However, it is hardly surprising that there are considerable differences in the species of plants which make up the communities in these various places, even though they build vegetation of similar structure. In western Europe, the majority of the heath communities have heather as their most important species, but there is great variety in its associates. For example, over much of Britain it is accompanied by bell-heather (or 'heath', *Erica cinerea*, Plate 2a), but on the wetter ground this is replaced by cross-leaved heath (*Erica tetralix*). In the north (Scot-land, northern England) blaeberry (or bilberry, *Vaccinium myrtillus*, Plate 2b), Scottish cranberry (or cowberry, *V. vitis-idaea*) and, often on the more peaty ground, crowberry (*Empetrum nigrum*) are fre-quent in the heath communities. To the west, from Wales south to Cornwall, Devon and Dorset and in Ireland the dwarf furze *Ulex gallii** is common, but from Dorset eastwards in southern England its place is taken by *Ulex minor** (Fig. 2.3). So, in the different geo-

*English names are inadequate to differentiate between these two species of furze (or gorse), since the name 'dwarf furze' is ascribed to both.

graphical regions, factors of climate and soil and other influences controlling the distribution of the various plants lead to the development of a variety of more or less distinctive heath communities. It follows that early in the study of any example of heathland a thorough survey is needed to reveal the distribution of the chief plant species and so to discover whether there is important variation in the community composition over the area. In all the major variants, detailed species lists should be made so that they may be equated with similar communities described from other localities.

Distribution of heathland

As already indicated, heaths occur in various parts of the world where relatively cool, humid conditions prevail but where trees are virtually absent, as for example at relatively high altitudes on certain mountain systems or in parts of sub-arctic or sub-antarctic regions. However, they are most widely represented in western Europe where there are, or until recently have been, extensive tracts of heath in lowland districts as well as in the uplands. The 'heath region' is outlined in Fig. 2.4, and extends from the extreme west of southern Norway, through southwest Sweden, Denmark, the North German

Fig. 2.3. Heather with dwarf furze (*Ulex minor*). Dorset, S. England.

plain (Fig. 2.1), The Netherlands and Belgium, to parts of northern and western France, reaching its southern limit in northern Spain. The neighbouring islands of Britain, and also the Faroes, are included. In the British Isles heaths are best developed in the central to eastern parts of the country and also in upland areas. Towards the west, in the regions of highest rainfall, they are generally replaced by peat-bog, except on the more freely-drained, steeper slopes.

When we come to seek explanations for the distribution of a particular type of vegetation, or for its occurrence in particular localities and absence elsewhere, it is customary to turn to climate and soil as the main controlling influences.

Fig. 2.4. Map of W. Europe showing (hatched) the heath region.

Climate

The map in Fig. 2.4 can be used as the basis for a comparison of the climate of the heath region with that of areas outside its limits. Such a comparison would furnish instructive detail – here it is possible only to summarize the main features. Broadly speaking, the annual rainfall in the heath region is between 60 and 110 cm, well distributed throughout the year. (The number of days with at least 0·25 cm of rain is seldom less than 115.) Periods of spring and autumn weather are relatively long, summers are seldom very hot (the mean temperature of the hottest month is generally less than 17 °C) and winters are rather mild. These features describe a cool-temperate oceanic type of climatic regime, one important characteristic of which is that for most of the year the supply of available water exceeds losses by evaporation and transpiration from the vegetation – or, put another way, periods of drought are short. Naturally, there is a considerable range of climatic conditions within which heathlands occur. The extent to which the climate of a particular example of heath fits the above description can be discovered by making a series of standard meteorological observations throughout the year.

Soil

Just as the heath region is characterised by a particular type of climatic regime, so there are certain aspects of the soil environment which are typical of heathland. Many of these can be revealed by digging good-sized pits, carefully cleaning one side, and examining the exposed profiles.

Perhaps the most obvious feature is that in many instances there are easily recognisable layers or horizons (Fig. 2.5). On the surface there is always a certain amount of litter – dead leaves, branch-tips and twigs, deposited by the plants – and below is a horizon of 'raw' humus. This consists entirely of partially decomposed organic material formed from the litter, and is usually chocolate-brown or almost black in colour. This organic layer can be very thin, or quite deep. However, unless the heath is growing on a deposit of peat (organic matter which has accumulated under waterlogged, anaerobic conditions), the profile will show that the raw humus horizon is resting on the top of mineral material. (There may be a zone, usually thin, in which humus and mineral grains are mixed.) The mineral material – stones, gravel, sand and finer particles – of heath soils has generally been derived from acidic, siliceous rocks, so tests will show that its pH* is on the acid side. (Heaths will not normally form on

*pH is a measure of acidity: the lower the pH value the greater the acidity. Soils described as acid have pH values below about 6, ranging downwards nearly to 3.

material derived from limestone, chalk, etc., with a pH above 6·5;
though there are exceptions.) This parent material may either have
been formed on the spot by weathering of the rock, or may have been
transported to the area as a glacial deposit, or as fluvio-glacial out-
wash, or – in the case of heaths on old sand dunes – as wind-blown
sand, and in other ways. Sometimes the type of deposit shown up
in the profile will suggest the nature of its origin; at others it can be
discovered from geological maps or glacial drift maps.

Depth   Fig. 2.5. Diagram of the profile of a heath podsol. (Fig. by E. A. FitzPatrick).
(cm)

Litter.
Partially decompose
    organic matter.
Black, plastic highly
    decomposed organ
    matter.

Olive grey with fain
    rusty mottling due
    partial anaerobism

Dark brown, thin
    hard continuous
    iron pan.

Unaltered   glacial d

Sands, gravels and similar materials allow relatively free drainage of rainwater – this is a feature of most lowland heath soils, and some upland ones as well. A full account of the development of soils of this kind is given in a companion volume to this series (FitzPatrick, 1974), and here it is enough to point out that not only is the parent material acidic, but so is the litter deposited by the heath plants and the raw humus formed from it. Under the relatively cool and wet conditions of the oceanic climate, decomposition is rather slow and incomplete. Also, deep-burrowing earthworms avoid acid habitats. For this and other reasons, the humus, instead of being mixed in well down the profile, accumulates on the surface, where humic acids are produced. These dissolve in rainwater as it drains downwards, and on contact with the mineral particles they mobilize iron and aluminium oxides and also other elements which are plant nutrients (potassium, calcium, phosphorus, etc.). These are washed out ('leached') from the upper layer of the mineral material. This horizon often stands out in the profile as a whitish or ash-coloured band because of the removal of iron which normally gives the mineral particles an orange-brown colour. Below it the substances (humus, iron, etc.) carried by the water draining through the profile are deposited, producing bands both of the dark colour of humus and of the rusty colour of the iron. Sometimes the iron deposition is so intense as to produce a hard 'iron pan' or 'moor pan'.

Inspection pits may be used to identify and to measure as many of these horizons as show up in the area under investigation. They can also be used to study the distribution of roots. The results will probably be quite a surprise, for there is a great concentration of roots in the upper part of the profile, mainly in the litter and organic horizons. Vegetation on these soils is, in fact, very shallow-rooting: for example it has been found in a Dorset heath that the upper 20 cm of the soil contains 92 % of all roots. However, this is perhaps not so surprising, after all, on consideration of what has just been said about the leaching of nutrients from the upper layer of mineral material. Below the organic horizon plant roots are confronted with a layer largely devoid of nutrients. The majority do not extend into this layer, although some penetrate it and pass into the deposition horizon.

The type of soil just described is called a 'podsol', and although it is typical of heathland there is considerable variation even within a single locality, as well as from one heath to another. It follows that one inspection pit is not enough when investigating the soil conditions on a heath, and widespread sampling is required. There may be considerable differences, for example, in the surface pH and in drainage and moisture content, over quite small distances. Where drainage is impeded, the organic horizon may be much thicker and more peaty, while instead of the mineral horizons described above the mottled or blue-grey colours indicative of anaerobic conditions may be found. Variations of this kind are always correlated with differences in the plant communities, and this point repays investigation using transparent overlay maps of soil and plant distributions. In places heath may be found on deep peat, but heath vegetation does not normally itself build deep deposits of peat. In these cases the peat has probably been formed in very wet conditions by an acid bog vegetation, rich in *Sphagnum* moss, which has given way to heath after drying-out at the surface, due either to climatic change or artificial drainage. Evidence for this vegetational change can be obtained by microscopic examination of plant remains at successive levels in the peat (Fig. 2.6).

Fig. 2.6. Pollen diagram, showing the decline of forest (tree pollen) and increase of heath (Ericaceae pollen) from Bronze Age times, at Dalnagar, central Scotland. Several temporary fluctuations are shown (see p. 15) before the final rise in the Ericaceae column and decline in tree pollen. These are associated with the occurrences of pollen of *Plantago*, a weed of cultivation. (From: Durno, 1965.)

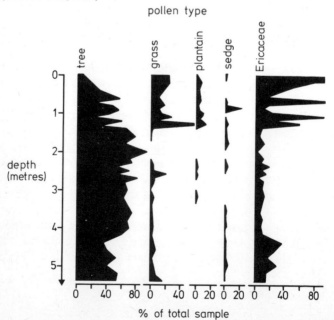

The problem of origins:
where history contributes to ecology

The heath region, then, has its own characteristic climatic regime and types of soil. Given this combination of environmental factors, do we therefore expect heathland always to be the result? Can we regard heath as a natural regional type of vegetation? Perhaps we can answer 'Yes' to these questions if we think of high altitudes on mountains, or certain coastal areas (Fig. 2.7) – but over the main heath region this answer would be ridiculous. It is obvious that where this combination of conditions occurs we can just as readily find various types of woodland developing naturally, as we can heathland. Indeed the woodland is generally regarded as the natural vegetation-type rather than the heath – coniferous forest in the northern part of the region (Norway, parts of Sweden and Scotland) and oakwood or beechwood in the southern part.

Another point here is that in some places we can see trees such as birch (*Betula* spp.), pine (*Pinus sylvestris*) or oak (*Quercus* spp.) readily colonising heaths, and eventually changing them into woods (Fig. 8.2). So we must look for some explanation for the occurrence

Fig. 2.7. A dune heath. Heather with marram grass.

of heaths, additional to the appropriate conditions of climate and soil. This is the problem of origins of heathland.

Where climate and soil are suitable, heaths can be expected to develop if trees are excluded. The explanation of the origins of heaths becomes an explanation of the exclusion of trees. In the 1920's some ecologists were of the opinion that, right from the earliest post-glacial times, certain heath areas had never carried trees. It was thought, for example, that the tundra conditions which prevailed in Jutland, Denmark, might have had such a lasting effect on the soils as to make them unsuitable for tree colonisation. However, during the last 40 years this question has been very largely answered by the development of a powerful tool for revealing vegetational history – the analysis of pollen preserved in peat deposits. Wind-pollinated plants, which include most of our trees, shed large amounts of pollen into the air each year. This falls as a pollen 'rain', and if it lands on the surface of a growing peat bog it is quickly covered by accumulating plant remains. The outer wall of pollen grains is very resistant to decay, particularly under the acid, saturated and anaerobic conditions of peat deposits. The intricate patterns which are found on the surfaces of the grains make it possible, in most cases, to be quite certain of the species of plant to which they belong. So, taking a core from a peat bog in or near a heath area, the pollen grain content of samples at successive depths can be analysed and a picture built up of the changing composition of the nearby vegetation. Wherever this has been done it has yielded evidence that the area was covered by woodland before it became heath (Fig. 2.6). The point in time at which the contribution of pollen from trees declined, and that from heath plants increased, varies considerably, but in lowland sites forest always preceded heath.

The problem now becomes one of explaining the disappearance of the trees. Some ecologists, especially those working towards the limits of the heath region (Norway, for example) have ascribed this to natural causes – in particular, to changes in climate. They have noticed that very often the change from woodland to heath occurred about 500 B.C., a time when it is known that the climate became more oceanic and less favourable for tree growth. It may well be true that in some places such as the Faroe Islands, western Norway and northern Scotland, climatic change was the main factor, but over most of the heath region more and more evidence has been accumulating to point to another influence – the activity of man.

This evidence takes several forms, all of them signs of human settlement, entering the record at about the time forest gave place to heath. Archaeological remains buried in the peat, thin layers of charred organic material indicating fire, pollen grains of cereal crops and of agricultural weeds such as ribwort plantain (*Plantago lanceolata*, Fig. 2.6), all tell the same story. Wherever we look – Britain, southern Sweden, Denmark, Holland, northern Germany, northern France – it seems that man played a large part in destroying the forest.

The pollen record is, in fact, sensitive enough to show that man's inroads into the forest were at first only temporary, resembling the shifting agriculture still practised in a few tropical regions today (Fig. 2.6). Evidently, small areas of forest were cleared by felling and burning and crops were grown for a few years before the people moved on to a new locality. Once the area was abandoned, there was a brief phase of heath (or on the better soils, grassland) before the forest returned. Sometimes the records show that this sequence was repeated several times before a more lasting decline in the trees took place, with accompanying increase in heath plants and grasses. This was probably associated with an increase in domestic grazing animals, which prevented the establishment of tree seedlings not only on cleared areas but also in the woods, so accelerating the disappearance of forest.

These processes did not take place simultaneously all over western Europe, but operated over a long period of time. There is some evidence of a shift from forest to heath in certain sites in southern England (Sussex, Hampshire) as long ago as the Mesolithic period (from about 4000 B.C.). Temporary forest clearance is known to have been taking place in Denmark, England, Holland and elsewhere in the Neolithic (from about 3000 B.C.) and where there were settlements of some size, as in the 'breckland' region of East Anglia, lasting development of heath began at this time. The process, however, started to gather momentum in Bronze Age times (from about 1000 B.C.). Some remarkable evidence has been discovered in Yorkshire (Dimbleby, 1962), by excavating certain Bronze Age burial mounds (tumuli). All over the tumulus and its surroundings the vegetation today is heath and the soils are podsols. But immediately underneath the mound itself is a brown forest soil, preserved in its original position. The building of the mound must have coincided with clearance of the deciduous woodland in the neighbourhood, so allowing the development of heath which in turn caused a change in the soil – except where the original soil was buried. Numerous Bronze Age tumuli can also be seen on heathland areas in Denmark and Holland.

With the beginning of the Iron Age (from about 500 B.C.) there is still more widespread evidence of permanent replacement of forest by heath in suitable habitats. It was about this time that the climate was also becoming less favourable for tree growth, and no doubt the two influences reinforced one another. Nonetheless, it was still only a relatively small proportion of forest that had been cleared, mainly in the more accessible localities. The pollen record shows that many of today's heath-covered areas still bore forest until well into historical times. Their origins are generally too recent to be elucidated with the help of pollen analysis so it is necessary to turn to the evidence contained in historical records, old maps and other documents.

These show that further forest destruction took place at intervals, for example in the Viking period (about 780–1070 A.D.), and during mediaeval times. Agricultural expansion in the thirteenth century was responsible for a certain amount of clearance, while the demand for wood both for timber and for charcoal to use in iron smelting made itself felt particularly from about the sixteenth century onwards. Many of the English woodlands were severely depleted of trees by this time, and in the seventeenth and eighteenth centuries iron smelting by charcoal burning extended even to the forests of the Scottish highlands.

While agriculture claimed some of the cleared areas, there was also an expansion of heath and grassland, both of which were of value for grazing animals. They attracted sheep farmers, whose influence steadily extended into the uplands, for example, in northern England and Scotland (Fig. 5.5). Their requirements for open country intensified the onslaught, and woodland continued to retreat.

While the wild life of the forest became scarcer, birds and animals preferring the open heath increased in number. In Britain, one of these was the red grouse (Fig. 5.3), a game bird attractive to sportsmen. Landowners were quick to realise the financial advantages of renting out shooting rights, and this too encouraged them to retain or extend the already vast acreages of heath and moor.

Summary, and a note on management

With so many influences all combining together and operating in different combinations in different parts of the heath region, the problem of the origins of heathland is far from simple. Certain points, however, are clear. First, it was a continuing process right up to the end of the nineteenth century, which probably marks the maximum extent of heath in southern Sweden, Denmark, Britain and northern Germany. (Since then other influences have led to a contraction of this area – see Chapter 8). Second, there is no doubt that lowland heath, while characteristic of a particular type of climate and a particular type of soil, is essentially a man-made landscape.

This leads to a final point: if heathland is a man-made landscape it follows that the continued existence of heath must depend upon some activity of man. We have already seen that if a cleared area is abandoned trees can often readily recolonise. So it is not enough just to account for the origin of heaths by an initial destruction of woodland; we have to explain how they have been maintained.

At first, the intensity of grazing was perhaps sufficient for a time to prevent the return of trees. However, it is unlikely that this was ever adequate for more than a relatively short period, especially because on the rather unproductive soils of most heaths it was seldom possible to sustain the initial high stocking with sheep. Probably from the earliest times man resorted to fire (Fig. 7.1 and Plate 4a) to keep the heathland open, and as the heaths became more systematically used in the eighteenth century and later, so management by burning became more regular. The effects of these management practices – grazing and burning – on the ecosystem will be considered in Chapters 6 and 7.

Suggestions for practical work

1. Determine on a study area. This should consist of a fair-sized area of heathland, or a region containing several smaller heaths. The programme of work to be undertaken should be adjusted in relation to the anticipated frequency of visits: for example, certain of the suggestions for practical work are particularly

appropriate for study areas near enough for regular day or half-day visits, while others are more suited to short, intensive periods of field-work which might be based on field studies centres. Many apply equally to both.

2. Discover as much as possible about the history of the study area. Public libraries, museums and local estates may have books, maps and documents relating to the area. If the origin of the heath was relatively recent, it may be possible to date it approximately; in any case changes in the extent of heathland in the neighbourhood in the past two to three hundred years may be revealed. Place names or farm names including the words 'heath' or 'heather' may contribute evidence in this context. Interesting information on changing patterns in the use of heathland may be unearthed. Many heaths are rich in archaeological sites. Published reports on these may also yield clues as to the history of the area.

3. If there is a suitable peat profile in the neighbourhood, a simple stratigraphic study and pollen analysis of a series of samples (see Appendix) may indicate the probable period of origin of heathland in the area, if this is relatively ancient.

4. Find out the main characteristics of the climate of the study area and compare (i) with the description of general features of the climate of the heath region given in this chapter (pp. 8–9), and (ii) with climatic data for places in Europe outside the heath region (e.g. from an atlas). There may be a meteorological station in or near your study area from which you could obtain data, but, better still, set up a recording station yourself and obtain records throughout a year. A standard Stevenson Screen is required (this may be built to the standard design, or bought), maximum and minimum thermometers, wet and dry bulb thermometers (or alternatively a drum-recording thermo-hygrograph), and a rain gauge. These instruments may be obtained from Casella* or Negretti and Zambra*, or other suppliers. Where possible, the number of days on which rain (or snow) falls during the year should also be recorded.

5. Using a geological map and any other geological information (such as a glacial drift map), determine the geological nature of

---

*Casella: Regent House, Britannia Walk, London N.1;
Negretti and Zambra: Stocklake, Aylesbury, Bucks.

the soil parent material, and the extent to which this varies over the study area.

6. Construct a soil map of the area. Soil pits should be dug to expose the profile (down to the parent material). When satisfied that enough pits have been opened to represent the main types of soil to be found, the details of mapping can be completed with the help of a soil corer. A representative profile of each type should be carefully described, the depth of the horizons measured and diagrams constructed. (The colour of each horizon can often be effectively noted on the diagram by moistening a small sample and making a smear on the paper opposite its position on the chart.) Record the pH of the surface litter and of each horizon, using a pH meter. This should be done where possible, at intervals throughout the year. Comparisons of moisture content of the upper horizons in different soil types may also be useful, providing the samples are all taken at the same time. However, such comparisons become more meaningful if repeated under varying weather conditions and at intervals throughout the year. Details of methods for soil analysis may be found in Jackson (1958), which should be consulted if opportunity is available for more extensive investigations of soil properties.

7. The variation of root content with depth may be investigated by using a post-hole borer to remove a series of soil cores. The roots may then be separated over a fine sieve using a jet of water to disperse the soil. They should then be dried and weighed.

8. The distribution of some of the main plant species or plant communities may also be mapped. Instructive comparisons are possible if separate maps of geology, soil and vegetation are made on transparent paper and used as overlays on a topographic base map (for example the large scale Ordnance Survey maps). Mapping of plant communities is sometimes difficult where these merge gradually one into another. However, boundaries are sometimes more or less distinct, as between heath communities and various types of grassland, or between damp heath where cross-leaved heath (*Erica tetralix*) is common, and dry heath where heather is accompanied by bell-heather (*Erica cinerea*). Such boundaries may be marked directly on to a base map.

A more systematic approach is to sample the vegetation at the intersections of a grid covering the study area, recording the distribution of a selection of the more important plant species. In practice, it is necessary only to lay out a base line, from which offsets are taken at right angles. Equidistant sampling points are located by measuring (or even pacing) from the base line, using a compass to keep each row straight. At each sampling point an area of say 4 m² is examined and the presence or absence of each of the selected species is noted. The grid can then be marked to scale on a base-map and, using transparent overlays, a separate distribution map made for each species by marking its presence in a sample by means of a conspicuous dot. Correlations may be noted between plant distribution and soil conditions, geology, or other habitat factors. If several species repeatedly occur together as a group in the same samples they probably represent a recognisable community-type. The areas which this covers can then be shown, as above, by dots marking samples containing the *group* of species (or most of them). It is important to have as high a density of sampling as possible, especially where there is considerable variety in the vegetation. Therefore it is more instructive to sample a *part* of a study area intensively than the whole superficially.

9. Make detailed species lists from each of the main plant communities you find in the area.

10. Make 'profile diagrams' to illustrate stratification in each of the main community-types. Cut a short trench, say 2 m long, so that the vegetation may be viewed from the side (see Fig. 2.2). To help in preparing an accurate diagram, a frame supporting a string or wire grid may be placed vertically against the cut 'edge' of the vegetation. The height of the various plants, and the arrangement of their branches, foliage and flowers is then shown to scale on graph paper. The opportunity may also be taken to observe and record the distribution of roots in the upper layers of the soil (see also 6 and 7 on the previous page).

3 Heather — a remarkable species

'Behaviour' of heather as a clue to understanding heathland ecology

It may seem strange to speak of the 'behaviour' of a plant, and the word is certainly not intended to mean the kind of conscious response to circumstances that it does when applied to man. Nonetheless, it seems to express rather well the capacity to respond in several ways to variation in environmental factors. Studies of the behaviour of heather have shown that it is quite a remarkable plant in this respect, and this goes some way towards explaining its great importance in the majority of heath communities ranging throughout the whole region described on pp. 7–8, although not in all. It is only in the more specialised habitats such as wet soils, boulder-strewn slopes and very exposed situations or high altitudes on mountains that it gives place to other plants. Elsewhere, heather is very often the dominant plant of heath vegetation. This is to say that its density and cover are such as to exert a strong influence on the environment in which all the other plants of the community have to live.

If we are to understand heathland ecology it is important to establish some of the reasons why this should be so. A first step may be taken by looking at a map of the limits of geographical distribution of heather (Fig. 3.1). The relationship between this and the map of the west European heath region (Fig. 2.4) is obvious. The geographical limits of heather include the whole heath region, where no doubt it was present as a native species long before the reduction of forest, belonging to open glades in the woods (Plate 2c) and to coastal and mountain habitats. When trees began to disappear, it was well placed to take over on the poorer, acid soils, in much the same way as grasses on the richer land. So the decline of forest made way for the spread of grassland and heath, and as far as the latter is

concerned this was partly due to the fact that the requirements of
heather for cool-temperate and humid conditions were met by the
oceanic climate, even in the absence of protective forest cover.
(The natural geographical range of heather extends eastwards,
beyond the heath region, into more continental parts of Europe –
Fig. 3.1 – but here heather remains confined to woodlands, per-
sisting only where tree cover maintains a humid micro-climate for
much of the year).

However, we must seek explanations for the 'aggressiveness' of
heather in the areas opened up to it, by examining other aspects of
its behaviour. A detailed study of all aspects of the ecology of a single
species – its *autecology* – is a vital step in understanding the communities to which it belongs, especially when – as with heather – it
plays such a key part. Much information can be gained by detailed
observations on the plant in selected areas and by experiments on
germination, seedling establishment and aspects of the growth and
physiology of the adult plant in the laboratory or greenhouse. The
rest of this chapter shows how information from these sources can
be built into our interpretation of heathland ecology.

Fig. 3.1. Map of the geographical distribution of heather.

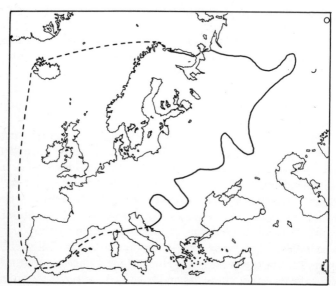

Seed production and germination

Among the properties of a plant which contribute to its ability to become dominant in newly opened habitats are a high reproductive capacity and efficient dispersal into the area. Reproductive capacity is the average number of viable seeds produced by a plant in one year. In heather this is not easy to measure, partly because individual plants vary greatly in size and partly because the seeds are extremely small and numerous. However, an estimate can be made by using a sampling procedure (pp. 34–35). One such estimate has indicated that 158 000 seeds were produced in one year on a single fairly large plant (Beijerinck, 1940), but few attempts have been made to check this or to investigate variations of seed production from year to year, or with increasing age of plant, or in different habitats.

Not all the seeds produced will germinate, but it is quite easy to find out the maximum percentage germination of a sample of seeds under favourable conditions. In heather some samples have shown up to 95 % germination, so – if this is usual – the reproductive capacity of the plant mentioned in the last paragraph would be 95 % of 158 000, or just over 150 000.

Whatever the actual figure, there is no doubt that seeds are produced in large numbers. It follows that they are very small and light (Fig. 3.2): average measurements are $0.6\,mm \times 0.35\,mm$ and the average weight is about $0.00001\,g$. Because of this they are readily scattered by wind, probably over distances of about $\frac{1}{4}\,km$ and perhaps further. This amounts to effective dispersal and, in conjunction with the high reproductive capacity, probably ensures that seeds are supplied in quite large numbers to any area close to a fair-sized patch of heather.

However, colonization of a new area depends not only on the arrival of seeds, but on whether or not their requirements for germination are satisfied. Tests show that in heather successful germination requires a continuously moist seed bed and is best in the light and under rather warm conditions, especially if the temperature fluctuates (e.g. above and below about $25\,°C$). Seeds germinate best on distinctly acid surfaces (e.g. pH 4–5), although some germination occurs even under slightly alkaline conditions (up to pH 8).

These requirements represent the very conditions which apply wherever acid soils, especially those with raw humus or peat at the surface, are exposed. Full daylight reaches the ground, the dark-coloured surface (Plate 4d) alternately gains and loses heat, while the partly decomposed organic material has a high capacity for water retention. In contrast, where in an established stand of trees or of heather itself the canopy casts dense shade and the uncompacted litter of newly-shed leaves or shoots forms a poor seed-bed, the seeds of heather fail to germinate.

Fig. 3.2. Drawings of·the seed, and stages of seedling development in heather. (From Gimingham, 1960.)

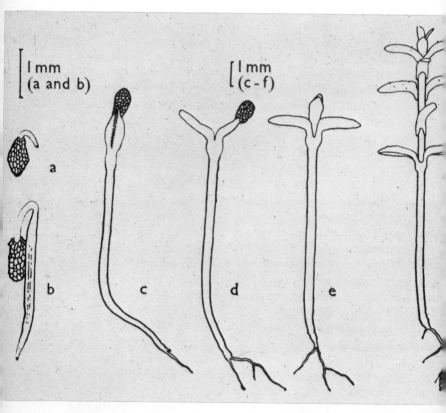

If a sample of heather seed is sown under favourable conditions, only about half of them germinate in the first four weeks. The rest require longer periods, in some cases up to six months or more. This property may be of some advantage to the plant because, if some disaster overtakes the first crop of seedlings, there is a reserve of seeds to germinate later. It also suits the time of the year at which most of the seeds are shed (November – December). In most years some germinate quickly, producing young seedlings (Fig. 3.2) which must then survive the winter. However, a proportion of the seed-crop remains dormant, germinating in the following spring or summer and ensuring the establishment of a new generation – even if severe winter conditions happen to eliminate the first-comers.

However, autumn germination and the passage of winter in the seedling state may be among those aspects of the behaviour of heather which tend to restrict the plant to oceanic conditions, where winters are relatively mild. Also relevant is the dependence of heather, during both the germination and seedling stages, on free availability of water in the upper layers of the soil and on a moist atmosphere close to the ground. Seedlings can easily be killed by exposure to a drying atmosphere. Only in an oceanic climate are all these conditions met over the greater part of the year.

The adult plant in relation to water and soil

As in many plants, the requirements for germination and seedling establishment are probably more exacting than those of the 'adult' plant. Once past the seedling stage, heather develops a degree of tolerance towards temporary restriction of its water supply. Plants can recover even if the water content of their green shoots has fallen for a short time to about 30% of normal. The woody nature of the bush, with rather rigid shoots and small leaves (Figs. 3.3, 3.4) probably has the effect of permitting this depletion without an accompanying collapse, or wilting, such as occurs in plants without these features. This may be one of the reasons why heather can occupy such a wide range of soil-types, extending from peats and other soils with high water-retaining capacity, to freely drained sands and gravels which dry out rather readily. However, it can be killed by prolonged drought and, at the other extreme, by waterlogging and lack of aeration around the roots. So where a heather-covered hill slope descends to a wet, peat-filled valley there is a zone, as the angle of the slope decreases, where heather becomes increasingly scattered and gives place to plants such as cross-leaved heath (*Erica tetralix*), bog myrtle (*Myrica gale*) and rushes (*Juncus* spp.).

Heather also suffers from what is known as 'winter browning'. This generally occurs in late winter, in clear windy weather especially if

accompanied by sharp frost. Severe damage is noticed only at intervals of several years, and the fact that it can occur even without
freezing temperatures suggest that the cause is drastic depletion of
the water content of the shoots, rather than 'frosting' alone. The
effects can be very noticeable but, although damaged, the plants are
seldom killed and new growth takes place in spring from below the
damaged parts. However, susceptibility to this kind of damage is
perhaps yet another factor tending to restrict heather to oceanic
regions.

Another remarkable feature of heather is its ability to thrive in
soils which are not only strongly acid but also poorly supplied with
some of the mineral nutrients essential for plant growth. From an
agricultural point of view, most heathland soils would be classified
as strongly deficient in phosphorus and available nitrogen and also
low in calcium and magnesium. That heather is successful on such

Fig. 3.3. Heather: the tip of a branch taken from a heather plant in October.
Growth zones of the past two years (and part of a third) are shown.

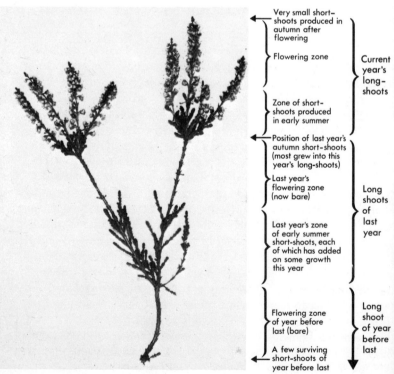

Very small short-
shoots produced in
autumn after
flowering

Flowering zone

Current
year's
long-
shoots

Zone of short-
shoots produced
in early summer

Position of last year's
autumn short-shoots
(most grew into this
year's long-shoots)

Last year's
flowering zone
(now bare)

Long
shoots
of
last
year

Last year's zone
of early summer
short-shoots, each
of which has added
on some growth
this year

Flowering zone
of year before
last (bare)

Long
shoot
of year
before
last

A few surviving
short-shoots of
year before last

soils may be due, at least in part, to its relatively slow rate of growth and therefore modest demands for soil nutrients. Its failure on richer soils may be due partly to the fact that they can support faster-growing plants such as some of the grasses and clovers, though it seems that high levels of plant nutrients, especially calcium, may be positively disadvantageous to heather.

Fig. 3.4. Leaves on the short-shoots of heather magnified about 50 times. The leaves are very small, thick, and permanently 'rolled', so that the margins almost meet, leaving only a groove communicating with the enclosed under-surface (where the stomata are situated). The groove is protected by hairs, and to a limited extent opens and closes as the water content of the leaf changes.

A further aspect of the biology of the heather plant of possible significance in this connection is its association with a mycorrhizal fungus which normally inhabits its roots and, it is claimed, to some extent the shoots as well. There has been a good deal of controversy about the significance of this association: recent work tends to contradict some earlier research and to suggest that heather can grow adequately without the fungus, but it is possible that, as in other plants, the presence of a mycorrhizal fungus improves the uptake of dissolved nutrients in acid, nutrient-poor soils.

Growth-form

So far, emphasis has been placed on physiology as affecting ecological behaviour. Morphology – the size, shape, form and structural
organization of the plant – also has its part to play and heather offers
fascinating evidence of this. As far as its form is concerned, heather is
a highly versatile plant with a capacity to adopt a variety of growth-
habits under the influence of different environments or treatments.

To understand how these variations arise, the normal sequence of
growth and branching must be followed. The young seedling begins
to produce lateral branches as soon as it is about $1\frac{1}{2}$ cm tall. These
appear in opposite pairs, from buds in the axils of leaves. But the
first pair of branches arises from the axils of about the 6th to 10th
pair of leaves, not the first (lowest) pair. From then onwards branches
grow out at regular intervals, so that by the time the plant is 2–3 cm
high it is shaped like a little pyramid (Fig. 3.5; Plate 3a). It can keep
this shape for one, two or sometimes even three years. However, the
first-formed branches (the lowest) grow slightly faster than the rest
and become horizontal, straggling over the soil surface (Fig. 3.5).

Fig. 3.5. Development of the young heather
plant during the first two years.
Notice the neat pyramidal shape, with
a tendency for some branches near the
base to become disproportionately long
and to grow out horizontally.

During the first full growing season, some flowers may be produced near the top of the leading shoot, and some of the lower branches
themselves begin to branch and to turn upwards, so starting to

Plate 1 a. Heathland scenery in a Scottish glen (Cairngorm Mountains). In the fore-
ground, a stand of building-phase heather in flower; on the slope in the middle
distance scattered pine trees are surviving, but the distant heather-covered hills
are treeless. (Photo: G. R. Miller.)

    b. Upland heath in N.E. Scotland. The remnant of natural pine and birch wood
indicates that forest would formerly have covered much of this territory. The
slopes in the middle distance show pattern caused by burning. (Photo: G. R.
Miller.)

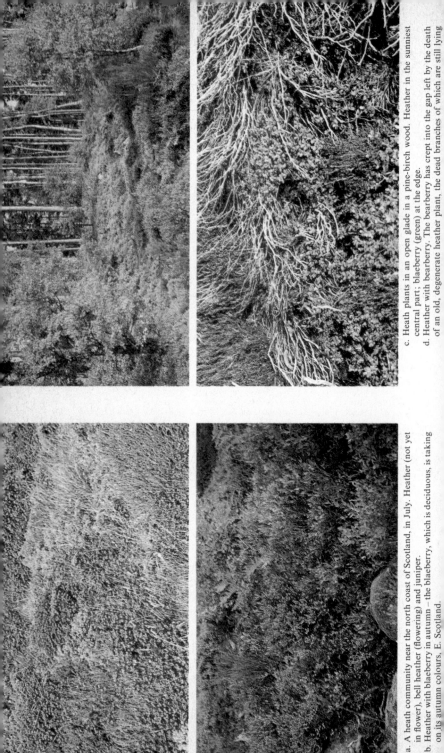

Plate 2 a. A heath community near the north coast of Scotland, in July. Heather (not yet in flower), bell heather (flowering) and juniper.
b. Heather with blaeberry in autumn – the blaeberry, which is deciduous, is taking on its autumn colours, E. Scotland.
c. Heath plants in an open glade in a pine-birch wood. Heather in the sunniest central part; blaeberry (green) at the edge.
d. Heather with bearberry. The bearberry has crept into the gap left by the death of an old, degenerate heather plant, the dead branches of which are still lying

obscure the regular pyramid-shape. The apex of the pyramid survives as a leading shoot only for one or sometimes two (seldom three) growing seasons, after which it usually dies during the winter and is succeeded not just by one, but by several replacements. At the same time some of the branches from lower down are catching up in length. So in the space of a few years the shape changes from a pyramid to a small hemisphere or dome (Plate 3b), and from this time onwards (in the absence of competing neighbours) the hemisphere grows radially until the whole bush is over $\frac{1}{2}$ m in height and perhaps rather more in diameter (Plate 3c).

While it grows, the density of shoots at the margin of the hemisphere is always maintained, and the way this is achieved is interesting. Examination of a branch from a heather plant shows that the shoots are of two kinds: (i) 'long-shoots', which are the actively growing terminal shoots on which leaves are rather widely spaced, and (ii) the 'short-shoots', which are laterals with very densely packed leaves (Figs. 3.3, 3.6). The short-shoots add on only a little growth each year and seldom exceed about 2 cm in length. They are, however, the main leaf-bearing, photosynthetic part of the plant – and they are evergreen in the sense that the leaves are not shed in the autumn. After two, or sometimes three seasons, the whole short-shoot is shed and contributes to the 'litter' accumulating on the soil surface.

On the long-shoots it is easy to pick out the growth which has taken place in the course of one year. This is made up of three zones (Figs. 3.3, 3.6):

(a) at the base, a zone of short-shoots produced during the first part of the summer

(b) in the middle, a flowering zone

(c) near the tip, a zone of very small short-shoots produced after flowering in the autumn.

Nearly always, the terminal bud of a long-shoot dies during the winter. Growth in spring is resumed by some of the small short-shoots of zone (c) growing out as new long-shoots. But instead of just one, usually at least two or three do this, and so every year each branch-tip seems to divide into two or three. In this way the density of the shoots at the margin of the bush is maintained or increased as the whole bush expands.

Working back from the tip of a branch, the annual growth segments can be identified for several years (Figs. 3.3, 3.6) – this is made easier by the fact that whereas the short-shoots survive for up to three years the flowers are generally shed at the end of the year in which they were produced, leaving a bare zone on the twig. Also, just below the base of each year's long-shoot there is a cluster of densely-packed leaves – the leaves of the zone (c) short-shoot formed in the autumn of the previous year, from the tip of which the new long-shoot grew in spring. These leaves may hang on for several years after they become dead and brown and even after falling they leave a set of closely-spaced scars, marking the junction between one year's growth and the next. Naturally, not all the long-shoots are retained to become thick, woody frame-branches – the weaker ones are shed as time goes on. As a result the annual pattern of growth becomes obscure in the lower parts of the branches.

Fig. 3.6. Diagram of a branch tip of heather, showing the past three years' growth.

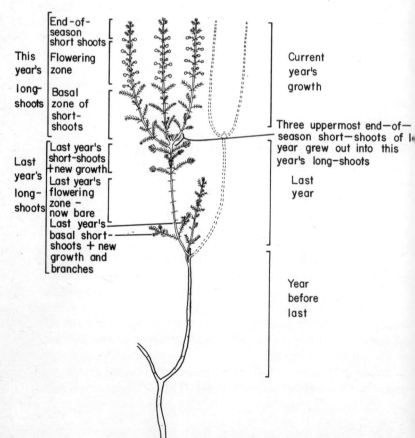

Response to grazing and burning

The capacity of heather to vary its growth form depends very much on this regular annual branching sequence. Take for example the effects of grazing. The edible parts of the plant are mainly the non-woody shoots (long-shoots and short-shoots) formed during the current year. The grazing animal (sheep, rabbits, hares, grouse etc.) clips off a varying amount of the most recently formed long-shoot, but below the cut what is left is likely to carry at least some short-shoots. Any of these can grow out into new long-shoots, taking the place of the old. Even if almost the whole of the long-shoot is taken, together with all its short-shoots, there are some reserve buds at the base. (These are buds in the axils of the cluster of leaves described above, belonging to the small short-shoot of the previous autumn). And even if the sheep bites off the whole of the current year's growth including this reserve of buds, there is an identical reserve just below the previous year's growth. In fact, so long as the heather plant is not too old (say, up to about 15 years of age), there is a reserve of buds which can produce a cluster of new shoots at every point where the stem forks or branches. The actual positions at which new shoots appear depend on the amount of the upper parts of the plant removed. The result is the same whether removal is caused by grazing, cutting, or burning, and can readily be produced experimentally (p. 37).

It also follows that, because of this behaviour, the plant is relatively resistant to repeated grazing. Each time the growing tips are cut back there is a stock of short-shoots ready to take their place, or even if these are used up there are groups of 'reserve' buds. And because every time a growing tip is destroyed it is replaced not by one but by two or more, the density of shoot tips is steadily increased even though general expansion of the bush is curtailed by the grazing. At its extreme, constant nibbling (as, for example, by rabbits) produces a low dome- or ball-shaped bush at the surface of which the shoots are very densely packed (Fig. 3.7). A further effect of fairly intensive grazing (removing about 60% of the current year's growth) is that the resources of the plant are concentrated into the production of new shoots, rather than being used in part for laying down woody material in the stems and branches. The successive 'crops' of new shoots have the high feeding quality of those of a young plant: in other words the plant is kept in a 'juvenile' condition.

However, heather cannot survive very heavy grazing, under which shoot replacement fails to keep pace with removal. One way to kill out heather is to allow cattle to graze it heavily.

It is precisely because heather responds in this way to destruction of various amounts of the upper parts of the bush that it recovers effectively after fire. In this case, almost the whole of the above-ground parts are destroyed, leaving only the base of the stem where it is partly buried in soil and litter. But even here there are groups of reserve buds at the lowermost branching points, or at the positions of the original basal 6–10 leaf-pairs (p. 28). These are often protected from the heat of the fire by the insulating effect of litter, moss or soil, and can give rise to clusters of new young shoots in the growing season following a fire (Plate 4b). It is on this property that the use of fire to manage heathland is based (Chapter 7).

'Dwarf-heather'

The effects of damage to the leading shoot of a seedling or very young heather plant in its first year or two of growth are also important. Because plants in this stage are tender and have a high nutrient content, sheep and other animals search them out, and

Fig. 3.7. Dense, dome-shaped plants of heather produced by constant nibbling of the young shoots.

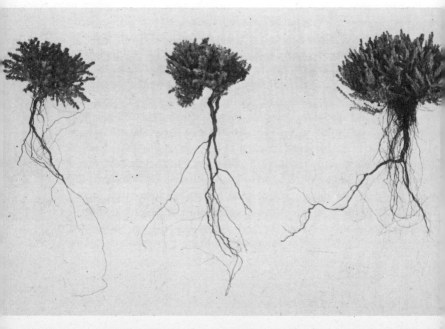

frequently bite off the tops to a level of 1–2 cm above the ground. In exposed habitats at high altitudes on mountains, wind may have a similar destructive effect. The response of the heather plant can be interpreted in the light of what was said above about the development of the young plant, and depends on the amount of the shoot destroyed or removed in relation to the position of the lowermost branches. It was pointed out that these tend to grow rather more rapidly than other laterals and to straggle over the ground surface. If grazing or wind destroys everything above them, only these creeping shoots are left to grow on. With continued grazing or wind-clipping, any new erect shoots are destroyed and growth continues in this low, spreading manner (Figs. 3.8, 3.9). Branches from adjacent plants mingle and eventually a dense compact mat is formed only a few cm deep. A dwarf heather community of this kind is typical of exposed mountain plateaux, usually at altitudes of 800 m or more.

Fig. 3.8. Samples of heather plants from different altitudes, showing effects of environment on growth-form.
   (Left) typical growth at low altitude (90 m);
   (Centre) mid-altitude (460 m), height reduced but pattern of branching similar;
   (Right) dwarf heather from high altitude (870 m), severe 'wind-pruning' has produced a mat-like form.
(Plants sampled by H. Hinshiri.)

Grazing animals sometimes nip off the top of a young heather plant so near the ground surface that even the lowermost branches are taken. Even then, as explained on p. 32, there are buds which can produce a cluster of new shoots: those buds which have remained inactive ('dormant') in the axils of 6–10 leaf-pairs below the lowermost branches. This, then, is a similar response to that of older plants after burning.

However, sheep tend to pull as well as bite when grazing, and frequently pull young plants right out of the ground. Even heather cannot survive this treatment!

Fig. 3.9. Experimental imitation of mat-like form, by repeated clipping to about 2 cm from the ground surface (compare with Fig. 3.8. right). (From an experiment by H. Hinshiri.)

The physiological requirements of a plant species, at all stages of its life history, set general limits to its geographical distribution and environmental range. A study of heather along the lines indicated shows also that morphological adaptability is of great significance in enabling the plant to compete effectively with others throughout a rather wide habitat range, and to respond favourably to treatments such as grazing and burning.

Suggestions for practical work

1. Make an estimate of seed production by heather. To calculate the number of seeds produced by a selected bush, wait until the seed capsules are nearly ripe (generally sometime in October). Count the number of flowering stems on the bush. Cut a random sample – not less than ten. Count the number of seed capsules on these. Again take a random sample – this time preferably

at least 25. Open each under a binocular dissecting microscope and count the seeds. (These are extremely small, so it is inclined to be a tedious task!) Multiply up to get an estimate of the number produced by the whole plant.

In a dense heather stand it is more instructive to calculate the number of seeds produced per unit area. Take several areas of $1\,m^2$ and count the number of flowering stems in each. Then sample as described above.

2. Germination tests can be carried out quite simply by placing seeds on filter paper in petri-dishes, provided the filter paper is kept continually moist (though not flooded). Time may be saved by using the seeds counted for No. 1 above and placing groups of 25 or 50 in one petri-dish. (Because the seeds are small, a fine paint brush may prove to be convenient for transferring them.) Experiments can then be designed to compare the effects of light and darkness and of various temperature levels, or fluctuating versus steady temperatures. (When comparing light and dark, note that seeds must be kept in absolute darkness throughout the germination period, and the temptation to have a look at intervals to see how they are getting on must be resisted. Very short exposures to light may have a significant effect. If it is found that light is important for germination, incubators used for testing temperature treatments must be fitted with internal lights.)

3. For experiments on the response of seedlings and established plants to varying environmental factors, seeds germinated in No. 2 above may be placed to grow on different soil types – for example, peat, raw humus, brown soil, dune sand, lime-rich soil, etc. Differing water regimes may be tested by growing plants in pots (all having the same soil, preferably taken from the heathland study area) and placing these in tanks so that some have a water-table at the same level as the soil surface, others at say 10 cm and 20 cm below it. The effects of shade may be studied by placing pots containing young plants under netting screens designed to reduce the light intensity at plant level by varying amounts. (Using a type of photographic exposure meter which reads in units of light intensity, rather than exposure values, the intensity of light at plant level may be recorded as a percentage of full illumination.)

In all experiments of this kind, young plants must be kept well watered and grown in a relatively moist atmosphere, for heather seedlings are sensitive to water deficits.

4. The 'relative water content' of the shoots provides a useful measure of a plant's response to variations in water supply. To find this value for a heather plant, cut off about 3–4 cm at the tip of a branch (i.e., the non-woody part, complete with the green short-shoots) and enclose immediately in a previously weighed, clean, dry, air-tight plastic tube with a tight stopper. The tube with its contained shoot is then weighed, and by deduction of the tube-weight the weight of the shoot is found. The shoot is then transferred to another similar tube containing a shallow layer (not more than $\frac{1}{2}$ cm) of distilled water, so that its base only is in contact with the water. This tube is closed and the shoot allowed to take up water, in darkness, until maximum water content is reached (12–24 hrs). It is then taken out, the base dried on blotting paper, and replaced in the original tube for weighing. Finally, the shoot is oven-dried to constant weight at not more than 95°C.

$$\text{Relative Water Content } (\%) = \frac{W_1}{W_2} \times 100$$

where W_1 is water content of shoot at time of sampling
($=$ original wt. of shoot $-$ oven-dry wt.)
and W_2 is maximum water content of shoot
($=$ wt. of shoot after taking up water $-$ oven-dry wt.)

Several replicates should always be taken and a mean value calculated.

It is instructive to follow the declining relative water content as potted plants are allowed to dry out over a period of several days (the water content of soil samples may be measured at the same time). If a series of plants is used, their ability to recover on subsequent watering may be tested, and an estimate made of the lowest relative water content which a plant will survive.

Samples may also be taken from plants growing in various habitats in the study area, to determine changes in relative water content throughout the year and in response to variations in weather, etc. (Samples may remain in the tubes for a while after cutting and before weighing. However, the time interval should be kept to a minimum, preferably not exceeding half a day.)

5. If the study area includes a hill-slope, set up a transect from top to bottom. This may be either a line transect, along which plants touching the line are charted, or a belt transect, e.g. of 1 m in width, in which the occurrence or cover of plants is recorded in successive sectors, e.g. of 1 m². (Depending on the length of the transect, records may be made for the whole transect, or at selected intervals along it.) At selected intervals a pit should be dug and the soil profile described. Samples taken from measured depths (chosen to represent the main horizons) should be weighed fresh and after oven-drying at not more than 95 °C. This gives a measure of soil water content, which is expressed as a percentage of the oven-dry weight of the sample, i.e.

$$\frac{\text{soil water content}}{\text{wt. of oven-dry soil}} \times 100.$$

A chart can be drawn up illustrating the 'hydrologic sequence' of soil type in relation to variations in the occurrence of the various plant species.

6. Compare shoots of heather from the study area with the description on pp.28–30, and with Figs. 3.3, 3.6, to make sure the normal annual sequence of growth is understood. Look for variations related to different habitats (notably in relation to altitude and exposure, or to grazing).

7. Using plants in pots, carry out experiments to imitate the effects of grazing, burning, or wind-pruning.

On large, well established plants determine the response to gentle pruning (use scissors – cutting off a short length of the current year's long shoots), medium or severe pruning (cutting off half, or all, of the year's growth) or severe damage (cutting the branches half way down, or just above soil level). In all cases mark branches for detailed examination, using coloured nylon thread or fine coloured plastic strip, and record by means of a series of diagrams.

See if, over a period of months, repeated treatment will produce the dense ball-shaped form described on p. 31, and whether clipping of young plants (e.g. small pyramid-plants not exceeding 5 cm high) as described on p. 33 will produce 'dwarf-heather'.

4 Cyclical processes and succession

Even in apparently stable and enduring types of vegetation such as mature forest there are dynamic processes at work. The biotic community of the whole forest may not alter much, either in the species of plants and animals present or in their numerical proportions, but in any particular patch of the forest the changes may be considerable. Following the death of an old tree, for example, a long time may elapse before a seedling grows up to replace it, and in the meantime the gap may be filled by a variety of other plants. A new micro-habitat is created, leading to changes in the animal populations as well. Sooner or later, however, the original condition is restored by the development of a new individual of the dominant tree species in place of the old. The changes which have taken place are cyclical and repetitive.

Cyclical changes of this and other kinds occur in many, perhaps all, types of natural, undisturbed vegetation, except those undergoing non-repetitive, successional change (see p. 48). This applies to heathland wherever it is not subject to management (such as grazing by domestic animals, burning, etc.), or has been free from management for a period of at least 40–50 years. Here the evidence of cyclical processes is particularly striking and instructive. They are caused mainly by progressive changes in the general form of the heather plants, as they pass through their normal lifespan of little more than 30 years. For convenience, four 'phases' can be recognised, and these are very important in understanding many aspects of heathland ecology (Watt, 1955; Barclay-Estrup and Gimingham, 1969).

The growth-phases of heather

The pioneer phase This is the phase of early growth, during at least the first part of which the form of the young plant is pyramid-like (p. 28; Fig. 3.5). If establishment has taken place from seed, such plants may be scattered (Plate 3a), whereas if sprouting has occurred from stem-bases surviving after fire, they appear in clusters (Plate 4b). In either case, the area of ground covered at this stage is small. In normal habitats this phase may last between four and six years.

The building phase   Before long the single leading shoot is replaced by a number of branches, adopting a more or less radiating arrangement from the centre of the plant. The form of the bush becomes more or less hemispherical, so long as it is not restricted by nearby plants (Plate 3b). This is the most vigorous growth-phase and the green shoots at the margins of the plant are densely clustered, so that very little light penetrates to the ground below. Usually the main shoots flower profusely (Plate 4c). This condition is kept up normally until the plant is over 15 years old.

The mature phase   In time, there is some reduction in vigour and the outermost shoots become a little shorter, with the foliage darker in colour and the laterals rather clustered. The even dome-shape of the bush is broken in the middle by the appearance of a gap, as some of the central branches seem to become a little top-heavy and to spread apart (Plate 3c). By this time the plant is probably reaching around 25 years of age.

The degenerate phase   Here the gap enlarges as the majority of the branches collapse sideways, particularly under the weight of winter snow. In time the central ones die, though the outermost may remain alive for a time. This is because throughout the life of the plants these branches have lain in a horizontal position on the ground and have produced fine roots all along their length, growing into the accumulating litter and humus. The result is a ring of green shoots produced from the ends of these surviving branches, surrounding a gap where the dead remains of the central branches are scattered (Plate 3d).

Cyclical processes

There are no sharp distinctions between these phases – each one grades imperceptibly into the next. However, as the form of the plant changes, so its influence on the conditions of the micro-habitat below it and around it gradually alters (Fig. 4.1). At first the young plant occupies only a small area. There may be a good deal of bare ground around it, so rain and light reach the surface and free air movement takes place just above it. At this stage mosses, lichens and other flowering plants are associated with the developing

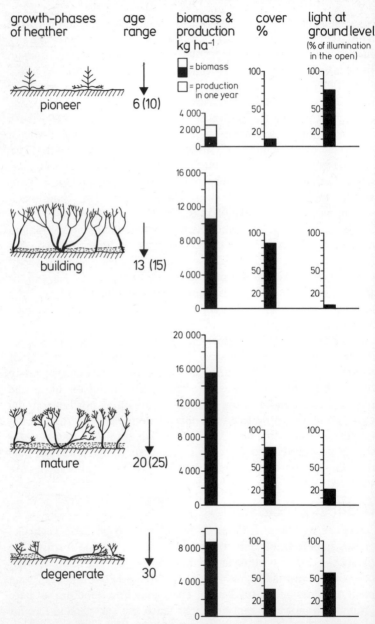

Fig. 4.1. Diagram illustrating the four growth-phases of heather and associated changes in biomass and production, cover and illumination at ground level.

heather. As the building phase develops and these conditions change, the plant becomes larger and denser. Light is almost completely excluded from the ground below, much of the rain is intercepted by the branches of the plant, and the air beneath the canopy is still and usually saturated. Few plants survive below the heather bush. Later, during the mature and degenerate phases, as the gap develops, conditions progressively revert to those associated with pioneer plants. The area of the gap is gradually invaded by other plants. First, a sequence of mosses enters where their light requirements

Fig. 4.2. The lichen *Parmelia physodes* growing as an epiphyte on the older parts of branches of a degenerate heather plant (Photo: N. Picozzi).

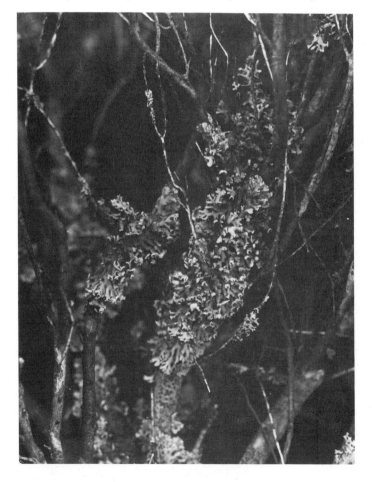

are satisfied. Lichens colonise the old woody heather stems as they spread out (Fig. 4.2, Plate 3d). As the gap enlarges, other flowering plants appear such as wavy hair grass (*Deschampsia flexuosa*) or species with creeping rhizomes spreading in from nearby centres such as blaeberry, bearberry (*Arctostaphylos uva-ursi*; Plate 2d) or crowberry (Fig. 4.3).

In time, young pioneer plants of heather may appear in the area of the gap, but their arrival is often delayed for varying periods, partly because – as already mentioned – heather litter makes a poor seed-bed, and partly because of competition from the other plants already established there. But unless some other factor intervenes, the cycle will eventually be completed and the process repeated (Plate 2d). The details of the plant species taking part vary according to the location and habitat, and these factors affect the time for completion of all phases of one cycle. This is seldom less than 30 years and in many instances may take at least twice as long.

Pattern in the community

One of the consequences of this process can easily be seen in any patch of heath where the individual heather plants are all of different ages. (This is referred to as an 'uneven-aged stand' and develops only when the heath has been undisturbed for many years.) Because adjacent plants are of different age, each will be at a different phase in its morphological development. The result is a patchy community, with heather plants of all phases side by side and gaps which may be occupied by other species. Such a community is described as displaying a marked pattern. It has already been pointed out that the effects of the heather plant upon the conditions of the micro-habitat vary in relation to growth-phase. Hence, in a patterned community there will be corresponding patterns in the micro-environmental factors, such as light, temperature range, humidity, air movement, through-fall of rain, etc.

By contrast, management by burning gives rise to even-aged stands. More will be said about this in Chapter 7, but here it is relevant to point out that, after a fire, pioneer heather soon appears over the whole burnt area. Because the plants are even-aged they all pass into the building phase more or less simultaneously (Plate 4c). Normally, the area would be burnt again before the stand had progressed beyond the building phase but, if not, the mature phase would follow throughout the stand and eventually all plants would

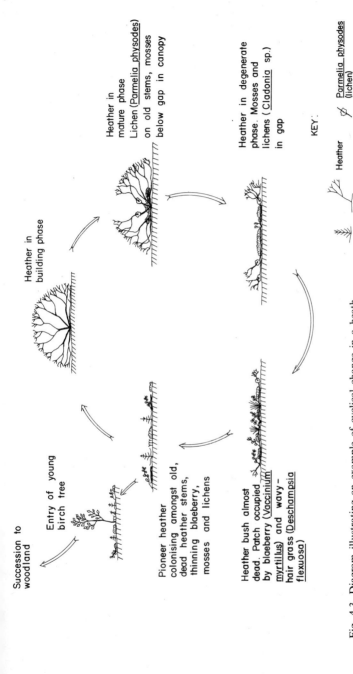

Succession to woodland

Entry of young birch tree

Heather in building phase

Heather in mature phase Lichen (Parmelia physodes) on old stems, mosses below gap in canopy

Pioneer heather colonising amongst old, dead heather stems, thinning blaeberry, mosses and lichens

Heather in degenerate phase. Mosses and lichens (Cladonia sp.) in gap

Heather bush almost dead. Patch occupied by blaeberry (Vaccinium myrtillus) and wavy-hair grass (Deschampsia flexuosa)

KEY:

Heather   Parmelia physodes (lichen)

Mosses   Cladonia sp (lichen)

Blaeberry   Wavy hair-grass

Birch sapling

Fig. 4.3. Diagram illustrating an example of cyclical change in a heath community associated with the sequence of growth-phases of heather. Top left – the entry of birch initiates succession towards a woodland community.

pass into the degenerate phase, with widespread dying-out. (The simultaneous death of heather plants over a considerable area is sometimes observed.) Under these circumstances, the micro-environment is much more uniform throughout the stand than in an uneven-aged community. As the plants progress from one phase to the next the accompanying changes in micro-environment also take place uniformly over the whole area.

Interactions with other plants

In describing the growth-phases of heather, reference was made to their differing effects on the environment just below the plant, and consequently on the ability of other plants to share this micro-habitat. Put another way, the heather plant reaches the peak of its 'competitive ability' in the building phase, when the majority of other species are excluded from the patch of ground it occupies. During the mature phase, this effect begins to be relaxed as the developing gap in the centre of the bush permits the passage of more light. Interactions with other species are least intensive in the degenerate and pioneer phases.

These changes can be shown in several ways. In an uneven-aged stand of heather, the numbers of different species associated with heather in each of its different phases can be recorded, and by means of an appropriate sampling method (pp. 50, 73) their cover and biomass* can be estimated and the changes correlated with the growth-phase of heather. An example is given in Table 1.

Dr A. S. Watt (1955), working on the heaths of the East Anglian breckland investigated the balance between bracken fern (*Pteridium aquilinum*) and heather in places where the two occur together (Fig. 4.4). In areas of dense heather his samples showed that the distribution of bracken fronds was strongly affected by the growth-phase of the heather plant: fewer fronds appeared amongst building heather than amongst mature heather, while the numbers of fronds in both these phases were markedly less than amongst degenerate or pioneer heather. (He also showed that bracken passes through a similar series of growth-phases and in areas occupied by building or mature bracken, the heather was at a disadvantage.)

Because interactions between heather and other plants are at maximum intensity in the building phase, even-aged stands at this phase, developed as a result of management by burning, have fewest associated species. This point has a practical application in connection with afforestation of heathland. When Sitka spruce (*Picea*

*Biomass = dry weight of plant material per unit area at any given time (see pp. 52, 64–66).

sitchensis), a commonly-planted tree of commercial importance, is grown amongst vigorous heather, the young trees instead of developing normally remain in a stunted condition described as 'check'. That this is due to some interaction with heather can be shown by removing the heather from the neighbourhood of the trees, when they are released from 'check'. Some other trees may show a similar reaction, although Sitka spruce is the most susceptible.

In Chapter 2, when discussing the origin of most lowland heaths from former forest, it was mentioned that if management is discontinued trees may reinvade. The trees concerned in Britain are, in the first place, birch (*Betula pendula* or *B. pubescens*) and secondly, Scots pine (*Pinus sylvestris*) or in some areas oak (*Quercus* species). Their ability to colonise amongst heather is also affected by the growth-phase of the heather plants: very few seedlings can become established amongst building heather, whereas the gaps in degenerate heather or areas of pioneer heather may contain numerous young trees. (It is possible to be misled into an opposite conclusion by finding young trees sometimes surrounded by dense building

Fig. 4.4. Bracken fronds among heather. A vigorous even-aged stand of building heather like this will prevent the bracken from becoming very dense. (Photo: N. Picozzi.)

heather. However, if the age of representative trees and heather plants is found by counting annual rings (pp. 50–51), it can usually be shown that at the time the trees became established the heather was in the pioneer phase.)

TABLE 1

Biomass of various components of a heath community in relation to the growth-phase of heather.

Growth-phase of heather represented in area sampled	Pioneer	Building	Mature	Degenerate
Mean age, in years, of heather stems	5·7	9·0	17·1	24·0
Biomass (g dry weight m^{-2}) of:				
Heather	287·2	1 507·6	1 923·6	1 043·2
Other vascular plants (dwarf shrubs, grasses, herbs)	179·6	41·2	52·0	83·2
Mosses	422·4	153·2	329·6	434·4
TOTAL BIOMASS (g m^{-2})	889·2	1 702·0	2 305·2	1 560·8

(Data from Barclay-Estrup, 1970)

The influence of heather on other plants is certainly most powerful in the building phase, but its exact nature is not fully understood. The density of shade cast by the heather bush is a major factor as regards smaller plants such as bell heather, grasses, mosses and lichens, but does not seem enough to explain the 'check' in spruce. Root competition has been suggested as a possible explanation, because the application of fertiliser – particularly nitrogenous fertilisers – can release trees from 'check' even in the continued presence of heather. Some recent research has introduced the possibility of another contributory factor – the release of substances from the roots of heather, and possibly even from fresh litter deposited on the soil surface, which inhibits the growth of certain other plants. If this type of interaction proves to be significant it might also explain the observation that where isolated plants of heather occur in grassland there is sometimes a narrow band beyond the margin of the heather plant in which the growth of grasses and other plants is reduced.

Invertebrate fauna

As in any plant community, large populations of invertebrate animals are associated with heath vegetation. As described in Chapter 5, some of these depend directly on heather, or the plants associated with it, for food; others are carnivores or feeders on litter or organic material in the soil. All are influenced by the micro-environment, but in varying ways. Hence they are bound to respond to the changes in food supply and in environmental conditions which accompany the morphological changes in the heather plant.

For example, insects which feed in the heather canopy such as frog-hoppers, Psyllid bugs, certain mites, the heather beetle (*Lochmaea suturalis*), or the caterpillars of some moths such as the northern eggar, are generally encountered in greatest numbers per unit area in building and mature heather, where the canopy is densest and its biomass at a maximum. Litter-inhabiting organisms – notably various mites and springtails – may increase in numbers throughout the sequence as the quantity of accumulated litter rises. As far as the micro-environment is concerned, shaded and sheltered conditions prevail at ground level under building and mature heather, favouring animals such as centipedes and millipedes; whereas light and greater variations in temperature and humidity are associated with pioneer and degenerate heather, attracting certain beetles (especially the rove-beetles, Staphylinidae), ants, those spiders which do not spin webs but hunt their prey, some harvestmen (Opiliones), etc.

These are generalizations and may not apply in all instances. However, they illustrate the point that as the growth-phases of heather succeed one another there are accompanying changes both in the food-supply offered to herbivores and in habitat conditions beneath the canopy. As a result there are parallel changes in the populations of small animals. Where all phases of heather are represented side by side in an uneven-aged stand, the pattern or patchwork will be reflected in the distribution of the various animal species. Where, however, extensive even-aged stands of heather occur, there will be greater uniformity in the fauna of each stand since it will be composed chiefly of species associated with only one of the growth-phases.

Succession

Although many heaths owe their origin to the intervention of man, this is not true of all. Some represent stages in natural plant successions. Where vegetation is undergoing continuous change which is not repetitive or cyclical, this is described as plant succession. The development of coastal sand dunes is an example of plant succession, which under certain conditions includes a heath stage. The first permanent colonists of fore-shore sand are generally grasses – notably the sand couch grass (*Agropyron junceiforme*) and the marram grass (*Ammophila arenaria*). Each of these causes alteration to the local environment, by accumulating blown sand, contributing dead parts which produce humus, casting shade, and in various other ways. Each in turn eventually makes conditions unfavourable for itself, but progressively more favourable for another species or community to invade and take its place. Associated changes in vegetation and habitat, the latter often caused by the former, are typical of most successions. In the case of sand dunes, the growth of marram grass is the chief cause of dune-building, but when sand accumulation begins to slow down, many other plants can colonise the sand surface amongst the tussocks of marram. Mosses, grasses, rosette plants and legumes appear and eventually a turf forms, completely covering the surface. At this stage the marram declines in vigour and it is then that heather (and sometimes bell heather) may establish, at first as isolated plants. Later these coalesce to form an extensive dune heath (Fig. 2.7). This will not occur on dunes rich in calcium carbonate derived from shell fragments, nor where grazing by rabbits or other animals is heavy, but elsewhere the developing soil may become acid at this stage, so permitting the entry of heather.

All of this may take a long time – probably at least 100 years, perhaps more. Luckily it is not necessary to wait that long for evidence that this kind of successional change is taking place. Wherever there is a fair supply of fresh sand available to be blown against the dunes, their leading edge will be at an earlier stage of succession than the more sheltered, landward slope. A transect passing inland from the beach will therefore cross a series of zones of vegetation, and these zones – in the order they are crossed – represent the stages in succession which would take place, in the course of time, on any particular spot. Furthermore, new dunes may begin to form to seaward of existing ridges and a series of parallel dunes may develop.

Although this may upset the regular sequence of zones just described, it offers a set of complete dunes of increasing age on passing inland which again may be used to reconstruct the stages of plant succession.

Heath may also appear as a stage in the natural succession of certain types of acid bog. Where a bog has formed in a valley or hollow receiving water which has drained through acid soils, peat-forming vegetation develops, in which *Sphagnum* moss often plays a major part. The peat surface builds up and unless rainfall is sufficient to raise the water-table correspondingly, in time the peat surface may dry out and become aerated. At this stage, heather, probably already sparsely present in the bog vegetation, may become dominant. Evidence for this type of change is even easier to obtain than in the case of sand-dunes, for the vegetation records its own history in the peat which often contains quite recognisable plant parts. The side of a small hole in the peat will reveal the change from a rather light brown material composed mainly of small leaves, readily identified under the microscope as belonging to *Sphagnum*, to a darker chocolate-brown material containing twigs of heather.

The fact that heaths can arise in the course of plant succession does not imply that they are the end product. There is ample evidence that is not so. It has already been shown in this chapter that trees such as birch can colonise heaths, if there are seed-parents nearby. This applies equally to heaths which have developed as part of the sand dune or bog successions and to those which have been produced by man as a result of forest destruction. They remain as heaths only if managed by burning and grazing. If left to themselves, they will generally undergo succession to scrub or woodland (Fig. 8.2). The speed of this change varies according to the availability of tree seed and the nature of the soil and other habitat factors. As described above, entry of shrubs or trees is restricted until the heather stand has become patchy with plenty of gaps. If for any reason the arrival of shrubs and trees is further delayed, there may be several cycles of the repetitive kind described above. Eventually shrubs and young trees may establish in sufficient numbers to produce thickets and finally dense scrub or woodland. During this time heather disappears and when the birch is joined either by pine or oak, as the case may be, the rate of further overall change in the vegetation becomes imperceptibly slow. But for reasons to be considered in later chapters there are nowadays very few places where these successional changes from heath to scrub or woodland can be studied.

Suggestions for practical work

1. Using the descriptions given on pp. 38–39, and Plate 3a–d, identify the four growth-phases of heather in the study area. These may be found either (a) side-by-side in an unmanaged, uneven-aged stand, or (b) each in more or less extensive even-aged patches in an area which is managed for burning.

2. If all phases can be found close together in an uneven-aged stand, samples taken in heather of each phase can be used to build up a picture of changes in the plant community accompanying the sequence of growth-phases. Using quadrats* divided into a grid with string, the cover contributed by heather and the positions of all other species can be charted accurately on to graph paper. 1 m^2 is a convenient quadrat size. In sites chosen to contain pioneer plants, and to some extent with the other phases, this area will include parts of neighbouring plants, but in many cases an individual bush may spread to cover most, if not all, of 1 m^2 by the time it reaches the end of the building phase.

   Look for evidence which may suggest that the sequence of phases, and associated vegetational changes, repeat themselves cyclically – e.g. the presence of young pioneer heather in gaps left by disintegration of the centres of old degenerate bushes.

   A sketch map of a larger area, say 4 m × 4 m, will usefully indicate the pattern or patchwork of an uneven-aged stand.

3. Where managed, even-aged stands are available, the composition of the vegetation at each phase may be analysed using a number of rather smaller samples, e.g. $\frac{1}{4}$ or $\frac{1}{10}$ m^2. The cover of each species may be estimated, or simply a record made of its occurrence to give a measure of frequency (i.e. % occurrence in samples of a given size). For frequency *at least* 25 samples should be taken; for an approximate mean value for cover of the chief species rather fewer – say 10 – will do. Note differences in the total number of plant species associated with heather in each of its phases, and in the cover of mosses and lichens.

4. In connection with nos. 2 and 3 above, the age of the plants should be estimated. Take a sample of ten of the larger stems, cutting as near the base as possible. Smooth the cut end with a very sharp knife or razor blade and examine under a powerful hand lens or

---

*quadrat: a frame of wood, metal or wire, usually square or rectangular, used to mark out a vegetation sample of a given area.

low-power dissecting microscope. The annual rings, although not very distinct, can usually be counted with fair accuracy, giving an estimate of the plant's age to within two or three years.

5. Maximum and minimum thermometers, and light meters (see Chapter 3, p. 35, no. 3), may be placed in position below plants or stands of heather of each growth-phase, to demonstrate the different micro-climatic conditions associated with each phase. (Note – when using light meters for this purpose it is best to choose uniformly overcast days, with diffused light, rather than sunny days. The light intensity reaching ground level is expressed as a percentage of full illumination.)

6. If tree seedlings are present in any part of the study area, devise an investigation to see whether they became established in greater numbers in areas occupied by heather of any one phase rather than the others, or perhaps colonised after a fire.

7. If the study area is a dune heath, mark out and investigate a transect extending from the dune vegetation on the seaward side, into the heather. Look for evidence of spread of heather into the dune community. Comparative records of pH and organic matter content of the soil surface along the transect will give some indication of the soil changes associated with the development of dune heath.

8. If the study area consists of heath overlying peat, examine pits or other profiles of the peat to discover whether the plant remains indicate successional change from, for example, *Sphagnum* bog to heath (p. 49).

5 The heathland ecosystem

The vegetation and fauna of a particular habitat can be fully understood only in the context of their non-living surroundings. The
whole complex of living organisms together with their environment
makes up what is known as the ecosystem. In studying an ecosystem
we are not just listing the plants and animals and describing their
adaptations, we are examining the processes which go on – that is
to say the interactions of living organisms among themselves and
with the physical and chemical factors of the environment.

Production and biomass

Among the most fundamental of these processes is that described as
primary production, which is carried on by green plants. Primary
production is measured as the amount of dry weight of plant
material* laid down in a given time – usually one year. In an annual
plant this represents its entire growth, but in the case of a perennial
like heather the production in any one year is additional to the weight
of plant material which has survived from previous years, and the
total amount present at any one time is referred to as the 'biomass' of
the plant.

The energy for this production comes from the sun, and the
organic substances produced are energy-rich. These provide a source
of food for herbivorous animals, which in turn are preyed upon by
carnivores. On the basis of these relationships the living organisms
in an ecosystem constitute a series of *trophic levels*, as follows:

1) Primary producers (the green plants)
2) Herbivores
3) First carnivores   } Secondary producers – (animals)
4) Second carnivores, etc.

(The numbers of 'levels' of carnivores varies from one ecosystem to
another.)

*i.e. weight after drying in an oven at 95 °C.

Nutrient cycling

There is a continuous contribution of dead organic matter to the soil in the form of a litter of leaves, stems and flowers, which falls from the vegetation, faeces and dead bodies of animals, and dead plant roots. A start to the breakdown of this is made by soil animals, notably earthworms (if present), mites (Acarina) and springtails (Collembola), which use it for food. However, further decay is due to another group of organisms of great importance in the ecosystem – the 'decomposers' – bacteria and fungi. Depending on the rate of decay there may be some overall accumulation of litter and raw humus, but decomposition gradually releases mineral nutrients into the soil, rendering at least some of them available for uptake by living plant roots.

Any ecosystem can be thought of as having, at a particular time, a fund of mineral nutrients – calcium, magnesium, potassium, phosphorus, nitrogen, etc. A part of this fund is located in the soil and a part in the vegetation and animals. In a woodland the fund is approximately equally divided between the vegetation and the soil; a ratio of about 1:1 would be typical. In a rich grassland this ratio might be 1:3, but in a heath there is usually much less of the fund in the vegetation than in the soil, perhaps about 1:15. This is because the vegetation is slow-growing and deposits an acid litter which does not encourage rapid decomposition. As a result, a layer of raw humus gradually accumulates at the surface.

Mineral nutrients circulate in an ecosystem: 'nutrient cycling' is a characteristic of all ecosystems. Plants take up available nutrient elements from the soil. When plants are eaten, part of their nutrient content passes on to a higher trophic level, eventually finding its way back as a result of the decomposition of faeces and carcasses; the rest is returned in the plant litter. If, as in most heaths, the rate of accumulation of organic matter in the soil exceeds the rate of breakdown, it follows that a proportion of the total fund of nutrients is slowly being 'locked up' in a form unavailable to plants.

However, no ecosystem is an entirely closed system, completely cut off from its surroundings. In addition to the cycling just described there may be various inputs of nutrients to the system and various losses (Fig. 5.1). Depending upon which is the greater, an ecosystem may be gradually enriched with, or depleted of nutrients. Some examples of the nutrient inputs and losses in heathland ecosystems will be given at the end of this chapter.

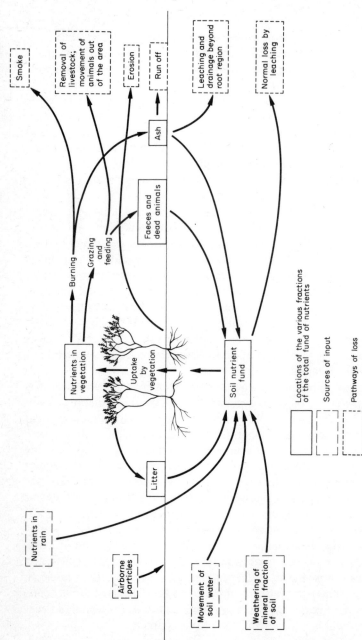

Fig. 5.1. Diagram of the main sources of input and loss to the nutrient 'fund' in heathland vegetation and soil. (From: Gimingham, 1972.)

Trophic levels and food webs in heathland

The chief primary producer in most heathland communities is heather. In some cases this plant alone accounts for the bulk of all primary production, in others a significant proportion is contributed by other species. Where mosses or lichens are present in quantity their annual production may constitute an important fraction of the total.

The secondary producers, or herbivores, include not only the more obvious grazing animals but also the less conspicuous though often extremely numerous invertebrate animals (Fig. 5.2). As mentioned on p. 47, some of these feed on the leaves and young green shoots of heather. They include mites, springtails and thrips (Thysanoptera) – all very small and not readily observed, but present usually in large numbers. Well hidden in the axils of leaves are Psyllids, but more easily seen are leaf-bugs (Hemiptera) and leaf-hoppers, or the frog-hopper which surrounds itself with a froth of bubbles (so acquiring the name of 'spittlebug'). Psyllids, leaf-hoppers and frog-hoppers belong to the group of insects named Homoptera and feed by sucking sap from the plant. Among the more striking insects which eat the young leaf-bearing shoots of heather are moth caterpillars (Lepidoptera), some of them large and hairy such as the northern eggar and the emperor moth (the flask-shaped silky cocoon in which the latter pupates is sometimes to be seen attached to heather shoots). Both larvae and adults of the heather beetle eat the shoots, sometimes in numbers sufficient to damage a patch of heather severely, and to merit description as a pest. Other invertebrate herbivores live in or on the soil, feeding on litter which falls from above – chief among these are mites and springtails.

Grazing animals include the domestic sheep (Fig. 5.5) and sometimes cattle, but a variety of wild animals and birds also graze on heather – rabbits, mountain hares (alternatively known as the blue hare or alpine hare), red deer (Fig. 5.6), and red grouse (Figs. 5.3, 5.4). Further reference to some of these, especially sheep and grouse, will be made in Chapter 6. Mice and voles are also vegetarian but probably depend on grasses and other herbs rather than heather.

The herbivores support populations of carnivores. Invertebrate herbivores, for example, are preyed upon by spiders, harvestmen and beetle larvae, or parasitised by Hymenoptera. Web-spinning spiders catch flies (Diptera) and small Hymenoptera in the heather

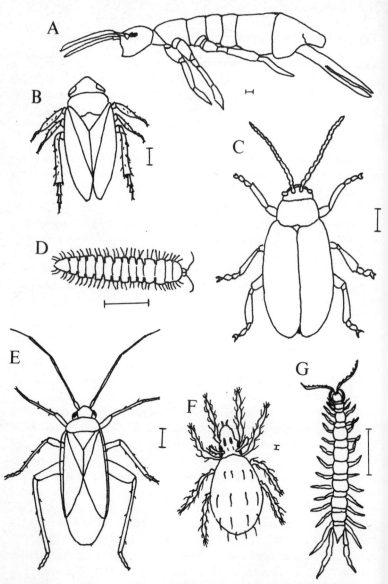

Fig. 5.2. Illustrations of some heathland invertebrate animals. A. springtail (Collembola); B. frog-hopper or 'spittlebug' (Homoptera, Cercopidae); C. heather beetle (Coleoptera, *Lochmaea suturalis*); D. millipede (Diplopoda); E. Capsid bug or leaf-bug (Hemiptera, Miridae); F. mite (Acarina); G. centipede (Chilopoda).

In each case the line represents the animal's actual length (excluding antennae).

Fig. 5.3. The red grouse: a 1st year cock. (Photo: N. Picozzi.)

Fig. 5.4. Nest and eggs of the red grouse. (Photo: N. Picozzi.)

canopy, while other spiders search for their prey on the stems and branches or on the ground. Centipedes are also ground-dwelling carnivores.

A number of heathland animals and birds are insectivorous, such as frogs, lizards, shrews, meadow pipits. Since these eat both herbivorous and carnivorous insects they can be classed either as first carnivores or second carnivores – indeed this distinction becomes obscured. They themselves are preyed upon by higher carnivores: for example shrews may be eaten by weasels or foxes (which also take rabbits and hares), meadow pipits are eaten by merlins. The dependence of members of one trophic level upon another is often described as a food chain, of which the following examples can commonly be observed on heaths:

Primary Producer	Herbivore	1st Carnivore	2nd Carnivore
Heather shoots	→ rabbits	→ stoats or foxes	
Roots and foliage of grasses, rushes, etc.	→ voles	→ short-eared owls	
Heather shoots	→ insects	→ meadow pipits	→ hen harriers or merlins

Fig. 5.5. Blackface sheep sheltering among birch trees. (Photo: G. R. Miller).

Fig. 5.6. A red deer stag on wet heath in W. Scotland. (Photo: J. B. Kenworthy.)

This, however, gives a greatly over-simplified picture because few animals depend solely upon one source of food, while some (particularly the carnivores) may fit into more than one trophic level. A closer approximation is gained by constructing a 'food web', such as that shown in Fig. 5.7. This too is inadequate to express all the complex interactions within the community, but it gives some indication of the *niche* occupied by each species – or in other words its place and function in the ecosystem.

Production

The measurement of production at each trophic level is an important aspect of the study of an ecosystem. Most heathlands are managed to yield a useful product of some kind, whether it be mutton, wool, game birds or deer. For this reason, an estimate is required of the quantity of edible material produced each year by the vegetation, available as food for the herbivores. Other quantities to be measured are the proportion of this primary production actually consumed,

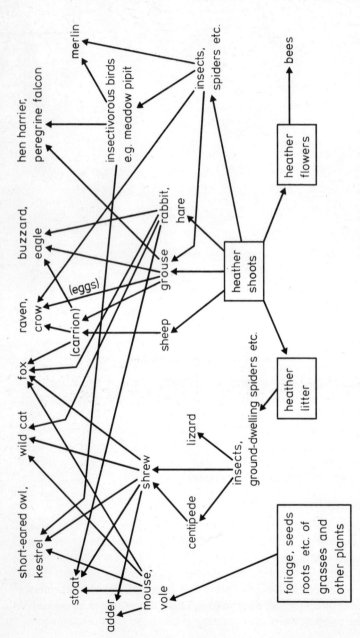

Fig. 5.7. A heathland food-web. This is a composite diagram built up from known relationships, and is not intended to imply that all components could be found in any one study area.

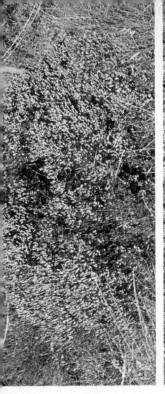

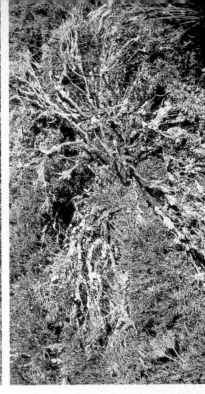

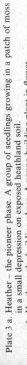

c. Heather – the mature phase. The central gap is just beginning to form.
d. Heather – the degenerate phase. Most of the branches have collapsed sideways; only the outermost remain alive. Lichens are growing on the old branches; mosses, grasses, and other plants have colonised in the gap.

Plate 3 a. Heather – the pioneer phase. A group of seedlings growing in a patch of moss in a small depression on exposed heathland soil.
b. Heather – the building phase. A young building plant in flower.

Plate 4 a. Heather burning. (Photo: J. B. Kenworthy.)
b. Vegetative regeneration of heather after a fire. Clusters of young shoots appear from the stem bases which were buried and protected in the surface humus.
c. Left – good regeneration, three years after a fire. The heather, in the late pioneer condition, almost completely covers the ground but flowers only sparsely. The edge of the fire is marked by the junction with an older stand – right – of building-phase heather, about eight years old and flowering abundantly

and the overall yield of animal produce. Only when these figures are
known can comparisons be made between the productivity of heath,
and that of other types of grazing land.

Primary production

A year's primary production by a perennial plant comprises the
growth of new shoots, increases in the girth of older shoots, root
growth, and the addition of new wood in twigs, branches, stems and
roots. It is not an easy quantity to measure. Often the easiest component to measure is the first – the production of new shoots. In
the case of heather it is a fortunate circumstance that the bases of
new long-shoots, and of extensions to short-shoots surviving from
previous years, are clearly recognisable (pp. 29–30). All the new
shoot-growth which has been produced during a year can readily be
clipped off from a number of sample stems, taken in late autumn at
the end of the growing season. The new shoots removed in this way
are oven-dried and weighed, and although the process is laborious it
is quite possible to calculate the dry weight of new shoot material
produced during the year, assuming none has been lost to grazing
animals (p. 74).

As already explained, this is not a complete measure of primary
production by heather, because it neglects root growth and the
formation of new wood. However, it does represent a substantial
proportion of the above-ground production, and it also accounts for
most of the edible material available to herbivores. It is, therefore,
a useful quantity to measure.

The annual production of new shoots does not remain constant
throughout the life of a heather plant. In relation to the size of the
plant it is highest in the pioneer phase when plants are small. However, it is generally more useful to consider production in relation to
a unit area of ground. In a heath community which has been protected from grazing and burning for many years, all growth-phases
of heather are represented side by side (p.42). For the stand as a whole,
the annual production of new shoots per unit area remains steady
from year to year, being the average of the various levels of production in each different patch of different age and phase. However,
it is much more often the case that we have to deal with even-aged
stands of heather, resulting from uniform recolonisation after burning. (All heaths used for grazing are managed by burning, see

Chapter 7.) In a heather stand of uniform age all the plants are producing new shoots at more or less the same rate, and it is possible to
make a reliable estimate of this production using a reasonable
number of samples. But the level of production for the stand as a
whole will change from year to year as the plants of which it is composed increase in age and pass from one growth phase to the next
(Fig. 5.8).

In Britain, dense stands of building heather usually produce about
2–3 000 kg ha^{-1}year^{-1} of dry matter in the new shoots. The exact
figure depends upon soil and climatic conditions and is probably
somewhat higher in the southern parts of the country than in the
north. Some investigations have indicated that once this level of
shoot production has been reached it is sustained, apart from minor
variations associated with differences in weather from year to year,
until the stand is at least 30 years old. It seems probable from other
measurements that there is eventually a decline when the plants
become degenerate (Fig. 5.8), but normally the stand is rejuvenated
by burning well before this decline has set in.

Fig. 5.8. Graph of heather shoot and litter production in relation to age of
stand since burning. The curves summarise information from a number of
investigations and all minor irregularities are omitted.

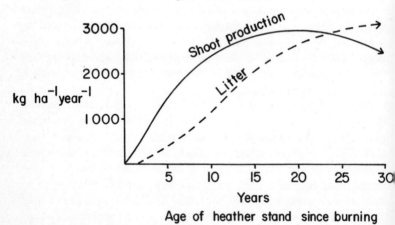

Naturally, the maximum level of production is not achieved
immediately, as a stand regenerates after burning. Plants in the
pioneer phase have not formed a closed canopy, and cover only a
small proportion of the ground surface. At this stage the production

of new shoots per unit area of ground is low compared to that in the building phase, when the ground is completely covered and growth is most vigorous. For example, it has usually been found that during regeneration of a stand after fire, the production of new shoots rises steadily over a period of up to ten years, from an initial value of between 50 and 200 kg ha^{-1}year^{-1}, to the maximum characteristic of the building phase (Fig. 5.8). In some instances regeneration may be so rapid that about 2 000 kg ha^{-1} may be achieved in the second season after burning.

Wood and roots

As a stand of heather gets older there is a steady increase in the amount of woody material in the stems and branches. At first this constitutes less than $\frac{1}{4}$ of the dry weight of the above-ground parts of the plant, but it rises to $\frac{3}{4}$ or more from the late building phase onwards. Year by year there is an input to the wood, but only a few estimates have been made of the amount. A figure of about 400 kg ha^{-1}year^{-1} is suggested, in stands which have reached their peak of production. Assuming about 3 000 kg ha^{-1}year^{-1} for new shoot production, this indicates a total above-ground production in heather of about 3 400 kg ha^{-1}year^{-1}. Very few heathland studies have attempted also to include an estimate of below-ground production. In one example, where heather was growing on a hill peat in the Pennines, root production during a year was found slightly to exceed above-ground production. Applying this to the figures already given for a well-developed building-phase stand of heather where above-ground production is of the order of 3 400 kg ha^{-1} year^{-1}, root production might amount to about 3 600 kg ha^{-1}year^{-1}, giving a grand total of 7 000 kg ha^{-1}year^{-1}. Such an estimate is approximate only, but may serve as a guide if measurements of this kind are planned for individual study areas.

The discussion so far has concerned heather alone. A comprehensive analysis of production in whole heathland communities requires also estimates for each of the other species present. Many of them present even greater problems than heather. However, in a few examples of heath vegetation this has been achieved. Figures from two of these, at high altitudes in the Cairngorm mountains of Scotland, are given in Table 2. It is worth noting that in spite of the harsh environment the level of production by heather (e.g. 1 632 kg ha^{-1}year^{-1}) is not very greatly below its general level in lowland Britain.

Biomass and litter

To say that heather produces about 3 400 kg ha^{-1}year^{-1} of dry matter does not mean that the total above-ground biomass goes up by this amount every year. All the time death is occurring of short-shoots, flowers, long-shoots and even branches. These may hang on to the plant for a while: from the age of about six years there is always a proportion of dead short-shoots and long-shoots remaining attached. Continually, however, some of them are shed and contribute to the litter lying on the ground. Measurements have been made of the quantity of litter shed by heather plants. In the first few years of their life the amount is negligible, but as the plants get older litter fall begins and increases year by year until it amounts to about 3 000 kg ha^{-1}year^{-1}, at an age of between 20 and 30 years (Fig. 5.8).

The increase of biomass in a stand in any one year is the difference between that year's production and the loss of dry weight through litter fall. Hence, biomass increases rather rapidly during the early years of the development of a heather plant and then levels off. This is easily demonstrated if stands of differing age are available within a single type of habitat. This is commonly the case on well-managed heaths where patches have been burnt in different years. Above-ground biomass can be estimated by cutting the vegetation from sample areas, drying and weighing. The amounts are then plotted on a graph against increasing age of stand (Fig. 5.9). If the dates of burning are unknown, age can usually be estimated by counting annual rings in a sample of heather stems.

TABLE 2

Production of various species in high-altitude heather communities: Cairngorm mountains, Scotland

Altitude:	855 m	915 m
Production: dry wt. of one year's growth (kg ha^{-1}) of:		
Heather	1 784	1 632
Crowberry*	23	—
Blaeberry	77	43
Herbs (mainly rushes and sedges)	374	460
Mosses	294	170
Lichens	33	128
TOTAL	2 585	2 433

*The hermaphrodite crowberry, *Empetrum hermaphroditum*
(Data from C. F. Summers)

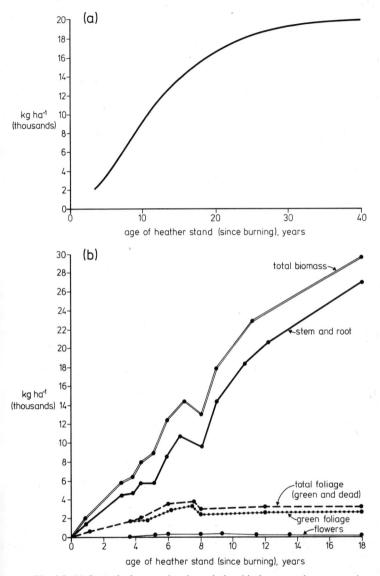

Fig. 5.9. (a) Smoothed curve showing relationship between above-ground
biomass of *Calluna* and age of stand since burning (Dorset, data of S. B.
Chapman).
(b) Curves showing total biomass, and dry weights of vegetative components,
of heather in relation to age of stand since burning (Sussex, from a school
study: Freeland, 1970).

In many – though not all – examples of heath vegetation, heather accounts for a very high proportion of the total biomass of the community. For example, in a Dorset heath, out of a total biomass of about 25 000 kg ha^{-1} in a 36 year-old stand, heather contributed $\frac{4}{5}$ or 20 000 kg ha^{-1}. It is not difficult to measure the biomass of all the other species in the community as well, at a given sampling time, if the complete vegetation cover is cut from sample areas and sorted into species before drying and weighing. This is an instructive way of expressing the relative importance of the various different plants in several types of heath community (Table 3).

Comparisons with other ecosystems

Primary production in heathland is approximately equivalent to that of the less productive temperate grasslands*. In grassland, above-ground production generally falls in the range 2 000 to 8 000 kg ha^{-1}year^{-1} (dry weight), sometimes exceeding the larger figure. Woodland or forest, however, may produce between 12 000 and 15 000 kg ha^{-1}year^{-1}, while in tropical rain forest the level may approach 50 000 kg ha^{-1}year^{-1}. On the other hand tundra, high mountain vegetation and desert scrub normally produce considerably less than 2 000 kg ha^{-1}year^{-1}, sometimes as little as 100 kg ha^{-1}year^{-1}.

Secondary production

Much less is known about secondary production in heaths than about primary production. The task of measuring production in the large populations of small invertebrates has not yet been attempted. Some estimates have been made of annual production by the larger grazing herbivores for Scottish heathland as follows (Miller, 1964):

Sheep   – about 17 kg ha^{-1}year^{-1} (dry weight)
Grouse   – about 2 kg ha^{-1}year^{-1} (dry weight)
Mountain hare – about 3 kg ha^{-1}year^{-1} (dry weight)
Red deer   – about 1 kg ha^{-1}year^{-1} (dry weight)

These are almost certainly over-estimates, for apart from grouse all these animals, even when grazing primarily on heathland, make use also of other types of vegetation. However, taking this rough total of 23 kg ha^{-1}year^{-1}, it seems evident that herbivore production is less than 1 % of primary production. (It is noteworthy in this

---

*But note that, as far as herbivores are concerned, the greater part of above-ground production in grassland is edible, whereas a substantial proportion of that in heath consists of wood.

connection that the utilization of available edible material by these animals is low, for example grouse eat only about 5 % of the available food in a year.)

Production by carnivores has not been estimated, but, taking into account their low population densities, the figures would undoubtedly be small.

TABLE 3
Biomass (sampled in late summer) of the various species
in 3 types of heath community
(Figures in kg ha^{-1})

	Heather-*Vaccinium* community, Aberdeenshire, 107 m, N.E. Scotland	Heather-Cotton-grass community on hill peat, 550 m, N. Pennines	High altitude heather community; Cairngorm mountains, 885 m, Scotland
Heather (*Calluna vulgaris*)	13 928	9 690	7 970
Scottish cranberry (*Vaccinium vitis-idaea*)		—	—
Crowberry (*Empetrum nigrum*)	334	420	130*
Blaeberry (*Vaccinium myrtillus*)		1	200
Cotton-grass (*Eriophorum vaginatum*)	—	1 487	—
Other herbs, grasses, sedges	252	13	370
Mosses	3 055	1 030†	880
Lichens	—	430	330
Total above ground biomass	17 569	13 071	9 880

	Heather roots	8 070
	Cottongrass roots	3 340
	Total below-ground biomass	11 410
	Grand total	24 481

*Hermaphrodite crowberry, *Empetrum hermaphroditum*
†Mainly species of *Sphagnum*

(Column 2 data from Forrest, 1971; Column 3 data from C. F. Summers)

Nutrient cycles, inputs and losses

Plants obtain their carbon from the air, but depend on the soil for all other nutrient elements. Here we shall discuss only calcium (Ca), magnesium (Mg), potassium (K), phosphorus (P) and nitrogen (N). Numerous other elements are required in small quantities, but those listed are of major importance and also serve best to illustrate the main aspects of nutrient balance in the ecosystem.

The amounts of each of these elements contained in the vegetation of a well-developed heath ecosystem can be judged from the figures given in Table 4 for a 15-year-old stand. Nitrogen, which is a constituent of all proteins, is present in greatest quantity, followed by potassium, calcium and magnesium in descending order, with phosphorus in last place. In general these figures reflect the demands made by the vegetation upon the soil for these nutrients, but it should be added that amounts contained in the vegetation may be restricted if a particular element is in short supply in the soil. In heathland this is often true of phosphorus, and may apply also to some of the others.

If, instead of an even-aged stand, all ages and phases of heather plants are present together, it may happen that primary production per unit area is just about counterbalanced by the shedding of litter

TABLE 4
The nutrient fund in vegetation, litter and soil in heath stands of varying age
Cairn o' Mount, Kincardineshire
(Figures in kg ha^{-1})

Age of stand since burning:	Ca	Mg	K	P	N
3 years: Vegetation	14	6	22	4	59
Litter	5	1	2	1	28
Soil	605	376	189	207	5 794
Ratio (V + L): S	1:32	1:54	1:8	1:41	1:67
8 years: Vegetation	19	9	34	5	92
Litter	11	3	3	3	61
Soil	662	401	216	207	5 951
Ratio (V + L): S	1:22	1:33	1:6	1:26	1:39
15 years: Vegetation	39	17	56	8	192
Litter	13	4	3	3	58
Soil	591	321	178	166	5 394
Ratio (V + L): S	1:11	1:15	1:3	1:15	1:22

(Data from Robertson and Davis, 1965)

onto the soil surface. Under these conditions, the nutrients are cir-
culating but the amounts contained in the vegetation remain more
or less constant. If litter decomposition is slow, as it usually is in
heaths, there may be a gradual accumulation of nutrients in the litter
and a corresponding decline in the amounts contained in the soil.
This, however, varies from one element to another depending upon
the nature of the compounds in which they occur. For example,
potassium is rather readily released from litter by solution in per-
colating rain water, whereas phosphorus and nitrogen are contained
largely in insoluble compounds and can be released only after
decomposition.

In managed heathland, after burning there is no vegetation left
so the total fund of nutrients lies in or on the soil. As the vegetation
develops it takes up increasing amounts of the various nutrients:
this is clearly shown in Table 4, which illustrates the rising quantities
contained in the vegetation and the declining amounts remaining
in the soil over a period of rather more than 15 years. During this
time litter is accumulating on the surface. From the three-year-old
to the eight-year-old stage there is a large increase in the quantities
of nutrients contained in litter, but from 8 to 15 years there is little
further increase, suggesting that by this time the decomposition part
of the cycle is returning nutrients to the soil almost as fast as they are
incorporated into the litter.

Normally by this time the stand is burnt again and returned to the
condition in which the sequence began. This type of management
superimposes a cycle of changing nutrient distribution, lasting up to
about 15 years, upon the natural cycling between soil, vegetation
and litter.

So far nutrient cycling has been discussed as if the total fund of
nutrients were constant and unchanging, in which case the tendency
for organic matter to accumulate in the soil rather faster than it is
decomposed would reduce the amounts in circulation. This, however, ignores certain sources of input of nutrients to the ecosystem,
and certain pathways of loss (Fig. 5.1).

A common source of input of some nutrients (e.g. Ca, Mg, K, P)
is the weathering of rock, stones and mineral particles in the soil.
Although no doubt this applies in heath soils, the contribution of
nutrients from this source is probably negligible because heath soils
are generally formed from slow-weathering, nutrient-poor materials.
More important inputs may come from the arrival of dust and other

particles blown into an area, or of water draining in from outside and bringing nutrients in solution. Unfortunately it is very difficult to find out the amounts arriving in these ways.

The nitrogen content of the ecosystem may be supplemented in a way which does not apply to other nutrient elements. Certain bacteria 'fix' gaseous nitrogen from the air, and after death and decomposition of the bacterial cells this nitrogen becomes available for uptake by plant roots. Free-living nitrogen-fixing bacteria are generally absent from acid heath soils, but many heath communities contain members of the Papilionaceae (pea family) which bear root-nodules. Examples are gorse (or whin, *Ulex europaeus*), the dwarf furze (*Ulex minor, U. gallii*), needle furze (*Genista anglica*), bitter vetch (*Lathyrus montana*), etc. Their nodules contain nitrogen-fixing bacteria and it is well known that the occurrence of such plants causes nitrogen-enrichment of the soil in which they grow. However, these plants are seldom very numerous in heaths and it is not yet known whether this is an important input of nitrogen. Research is in progress on this point.

Probably by far the most important input of nutrients comes from rainfall, which contains significant quantities in solution (Table 5). It is not known whether the total input from this source is retained in the soil: certainly a greater proportion is retained by a soil rich in organic matter than by one composed largely of mineral particles. In view of a continuing input from rainfall, figures such as those of Table 4 must not be taken to suggest that all the nutrients contained in 15-year-old vegetation have to be offset against the amounts contained originally in the soil. However, it is significant that rainfall contributes very little phosphorus, of which the supply in both soil and vegetation is low.

TABLE 5
Input of nutrients in rainfall in northern Britain.
($kg\ ha^{-1}\ year^{-1}$)

Ca	Mg	K	Na	P	N
7–12	3·6–5	3–6	22–36	0·2–0·9	6–9

(Actual values vary from place to place, but commonly fall within the ranges given.)

Losses of nutrients may occur in several ways. One of the most important may be by solution in water draining through the soil – the process known as leaching. Organic acids produced during the decomposition of heather litter have the property of encouraging leaching, and the dissolved nutrients may either be redeposited in the lower layers of the soil out of reach of the plants' root systems, or else removed altogether by way of streams and rivers. Again it is not easy to estimate these losses, though attempts have been made.

Wherever litter or raw humus is removed from the soil surface, this is a potent cause of nutrient loss, particularly of phosphorus and nitrogen. This means that any form of erosion may lead to serious nutrient depletion. Loss also takes place when animals move away from an area of heathland, either in the natural course of events, or by the sale of domestic livestock or game. Finally, the use of fire itself may result in nutrient losses. This is an important and controversial topic, to which a subsequent chapter is devoted.

With both inputs and losses in operation the question arises as to whether, in an area of heathland, there is a net gain or loss over the years. This can only be decided if estimates can be made of the major components and a balance sheet constructed. A great amount of work is involved, including extensive sampling and analysis over a number of years. Not surprisingly it has been attempted only in a few instances, one of which is summarised in Table 6. This refers to an area of upland heath on peat in the north Pennines and is not typical of heaths in general (amongst other things it is not managed by burning, and part of the area is subject to peat erosion). However, it is instructive in that it shows the magnitude of some of the components of the balance sheet. In this instance there is a net loss of

TABLE 6

Outline nutrient balance sheet for an 83 ha catchment at Moor House National Nature Reserve, north Pennines, England.
($kg\ ha^{-1}\ year^{-1}$.)

	Ca	K	Na	P	N
Outputs:					
In stream water	53.7	9·0	45.2	0·4	2·9
By peat erosion	4·8	2·1	0·3	0·4	14·6
Drift of fauna in stream	trace	trace	trace	trace	0·001
Drift of fauna on surface of stream	trace	0·005	0·001	0·005	0·055
Sale of sheep and wool	0·02	0·005	0·002	0·01	0·053
Total output	58·5	11·1	45·5	0·8	17·6
Input in precipitation	9·0	3·1	25·5	0·5–0·7	8·2
Difference = net loss	49·5	8·0	20·0	0·1 to 0·3	9·4

(from: Crisp, 1966 – modified.)

all the nutrients concerned, but a major factor is the loss due to erosion. It would be false to conclude that all heathlands are suffering a steady decline in their fund of nutrients.

In this chapter some of the processes which operate in heath ecosystems have been selected for detailed consideration. The remaining chapters are concerned chiefly with the ways in which man has adapted these ecosystems for his own ends, and with the effect of his management practices upon the various processes.

Suggestions for practical work

1. Construct as complete a food web for the study area as possible. This depends upon careful observation, undertaken as frequently as possible. The feeding habits of the larger herbivores and carnivores can be observed directly; those of invertebrates may require investigation by maintaining them in cages in the laboratory or greenhouse.

2. The easiest way of investigating heathland invertebrates is to trap them and then examine them in the laboratory. There are two main methods of trapping; (a) trapping over a period of time, and (b) trapping at one moment of time.

   (a) *Trapping over a period of time*   This involves leaving traps out in the vegetation for periods of time of up to several days. To trap animals living in the litter and on the litter surface, use a 'pitfall trap'. This is a vertical-sided container sunk in the soil so that its open end is level with, or slightly below, the surface of the litter. A useful way of placing these without causing too great a disturbance to the area under investigation is to bore the hole in the soil with a piece of pipe the internal diameter of which is the same as the external diameter of the trap. The trap should contain poison of some kind; for short periods alcohol will do.

   To trap the aerial population (flies, Hymenoptera etc.) use stickytraps. These can be made of fly-paper or horticultural grease-bands attached to a cylinder above the surface of the canopy. The specimens can be removed from the grease-band by dissolving the adhesive in warm medicinal grade paraffin. It is possible to examine the specimens in the paraffin or wash them out in one of the aromatic hydrocarbons (N.B. *NOT* Benzene) and then study them in alcohol.

   (b) *Trapping at one moment in time*   To trap the invertebrates in the litter, all the litter from a sample of known area can be removed. This can be done at the same time as setting the pitfall traps, by taking the litter which is removed in the pipe used to make the holes. The invertebrates are removed from the litter sample by placing it in a Berlese-Tullgren funnel. These can be purchased commercially or fairly easily constructed using a small, coarse sieve placed on top of a large laboratory funnel, suspended under a naked light bulb, and having a collecting bottle under the funnel. The light and heat from the bulb drives the animals out of the litter into the funnel and thence into the bottle.

To extract the invertebrates from the canopy, a suction apparatus can be used. This is extensively described on pp. 115–118 of *Ecological Methods* by T. R. E. Southwood (1966). It collects a large amount of debris and the invertebrates are easily removed from this by placing the whole lot in the Berlese-Tullgren funnel.

The majority of animals collected by these methods are best examined under a low-power binocular microscope, the samples being suspended in liquid in a white dish.

3. The above-ground biomass of a heathland community is not difficult to measure. It is best done at the end of the growing season, i.e., late September or early October. A convenient sample size is $\frac{1}{4}$ m², from which all the vegetation is removed. To do this, use a quadrat of this size and first clip round its edges so that branches extending into the sample area from plants rooted outside are included, while branches spreading beyond it from plants rooted inside are discarded. Then, using secateurs, clip all rooted stems within the quadrat at ground level and place all plants and parts of plants from the sample area in a polythene bag. Later they are sorted into species, oven dried and weighed. To obtain a reasonable estimate, a number of such samples is required – the greater the number, the greater the accuracy. If the stand is fairly uniform, ten samples may be enough to give a reliable figure for most species.

Where a number of even-aged stands, each of differing age, are available (as a result of management by burning), each of these should be sampled and graphs drawn both for total biomass per unit area and for biomass of heather and other chief species separately, against age of stand. If available, the mean biomass of an unmanaged, uneven-aged stand should be compared. (If records of date of burning are not available, stands can be aged with reasonable accuracy by counts of annual rings in the heather stems – see pp. 50–51). The growth-phase of the heather in each stand sampled should be recorded, so that the biomass/ age curve can be divided up into sectors associated with each phase.

4. To obtain a complete estimate of biomass it is necessary to include the weight of roots per unit area. It is difficult to get an accurate estimate of this, but an approximate indication may be obtained by digging up, as carefully as possible, the root systems contained in the soil below some of the sample areas used in no. 3 above. These are then washed free of soil (as far as possible), oven dried and weighed. The time needed for this job will severely limit the number of samples, and however carefully it is done many of the finer roots will be lost. Nonetheless, so long as it is recognised that the result is approximate only, it will serve as a guide to the underground biomass of the stand.

5. If, as recommended, sampling is carried out at the end of the growing season, and in an area free from grazing, some of the above-ground samples may be used for a partial estimate of production by heather. The shoot-growth which has taken place during the summer (new long-shoots with their attached short-shoots and flowers and additions to the short-shoots of previous years – p. 29, Fig. 3.6) may be clipped off with scissors, oven dried and weighed. Unfortunately, though not difficult, this is time consuming, so even with a number of people at work only a few of the biomass samples can be treated in this way. Nonetheless, it should be possible to obtain a figure for shoot production in each stand sampled, and again to construct a graph illustrating changes in the annual rate of shoot production with increasing age of stand. (Remember that increases in the woody parts of the plants and in their roots are not included in these figures.)

6. Litter production may be measured using narrow troughs made of rustless wire gauze, placed on the ground below the canopy. (A narrow rectangular shape is best, to fit amongst the heather stems – say 5 cm × 20 cm, with sides 3 cm high.) Litter trapped in these is collected as frequently as possible, dried and weighed. As litter-fall varies with the seasons, this should be continued for a whole year. Litter production per unit area per year can

then be graphed against age of stand, as in no. 3 above.

7. Herbivore and carnivore production are much more difficult to estimate. On some estates it may be possible to get figures of sheep production, or numbers of grouse or hares shot. However, these animals are seldom, if ever, feeding exclusively on heath vegetation, and shooting records are not necessarily a reliable guide to the size of the populations.

6 Grazing animals: biotic factors affecting vegetation

The plants occupying a particular habitat are subject to a great variety of environmental influences, usually referred to as 'factors of the environment'. Among them are the physical and chemical factors of climate and soil (Chapter 2), but also of great importance are the biotic factors – the effects of neighbouring plants and of animals. This chapter looks at the herbivores as biotic factors affecting the vegetation.

Where a factor operates at a steady intensity, the organisation and composition of the vegetation become adjusted to it and equilibrium may be maintained. On the other hand, a change in any environmental factor is bound to initiate some change in the vegetation.

Heath vegetation may, in some cases, have reached approximate equilibrium with certain populations of grazing animals, but more frequently – and particularly in the case of domestic herbivores – animals have played the part of initiators of change. In the past, there have been instances of the introduction of entirely new herbivores to heathland, as when the large sheep flocks spread to the heaths of northern England and Scotland some 200 years ago. As the fortunes of hill farming have varied, so grazing intensity has increased or declined. The vegetation has undergone continual change under the influence of this changing biotic factor. The effects of grazing are revealed by the changes which follow when it is introduced or removed, intensified or reduced.

Heather as a food plant

Mention has already been made (Chapter 5) of the larger animals which habitually graze on heather – sheep, cattle, rabbits, mountain hares, grouse, and red deer. Brown hares also take heather, while at high altitudes on mountains heather forms part of the diet of the ptarmigan.

Heather is therefore an important food plant: its importance lies in the fact that it provides forage of reasonable quality on poor soils.

It is for this reason that since earliest times it has been encouraged in upland and northern districts of Britain, and in other areas of acid, nutrient-poor soils. Further as an evergreen perennial plant it offers food in the winter when there is little to be found on most grass pastures. Even when snow covers the ground the taller branches of heather may project and enable the animals to continue grazing.

Of the domestic herbivores (sheep and cattle), only certain breeds are capable of thriving on a diet of which heather forms a large part. Cheviot and Blackface (Fig. 5.5) are the best known breeds of sheep in this connection. Although requiring access to grass swards as well as heather, they do well on areas which are largely heath-covered and often depend on heather for the bulk of their food, especially in winter. (Being hardy breeds, they can remain on the hill grazings throughout the year.) Much the same is true of Highland and Highland cross-bred cattle, though for them a higher proportion of food plants other than heather is needed, and if they are to stay outside during the winter shelter of some sort is essential.

It follows that the young shoots of heather provide food of reasonable quality. They are not as nutritious as good quality hay, but have a fair protein, fat and carbohydrate content. Mineral nutrient levels are indicated by the following figures:

	Ca	Mg	K	P	N
% of dry weight	0·34–0·48	0·15–0·22	0·56–0·76	0·07–0·15	1·1–2·1

These show that, apart from phosphorus, heather is a fairly good source of most of the nutrient elements (including calcium, which is often low in plants of acid soils).

Changes in feeding value with age

Analyses of the edible shoots have shown, however, that the concentrations of nutrient elements are at their highest in very young plants and decline quite rapidly during the first six years of their life (Fig. 6.1). After this time the levels remain fairly steady. It is not surprising, therefore, that grazing animals seek out young heather, though how they recognise that its food value is greater than that of older plants is unknown. Sheep tend to congregate on stands of young heather, cropping the new growth as the plants regenerate during the first few years after burning (Fig. 6.2). Larger populations of grouse are found where there is a high proportion of young heather on the moor, than where old heather predominates. Rabbits and hares also prefer young heather for grazing.

From this it might be concluded that the best way to manage heather would be to keep it in the pioneer phase – not more than about six years old. However, this ignores the fact that during the first few years plants are small, cover is incomplete, and production of young shoots per unit area has not reached its maximum (Chapter 5, pp. 62–63). Hence, two opposing trends are involved in controlling the feeding value of a stand of heather: the decline in nutrient content is offset by increasing production per unit area, at least until the stand reaches an age of about seven or eight years.

Fig. 6.1. Smoothed curves showing decline with age in the content of nitrogen and phosphorus in heather shoot-tips (data of G. R. Miller).

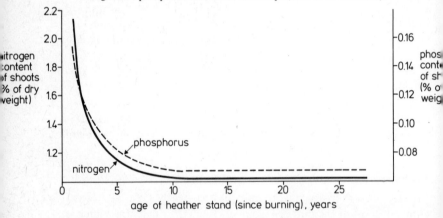

After this time production of edible shoots remains fairly steady, at least up to an age of about 15 years. But although the amount of available food produced each year remains much the same, the plants are getting taller and an increasing proportion of their bio-mass consists of useless woody stems and branches. (Grouse have to reach their food from the ground, so it becomes less and less accessible as the plants become taller and denser.) For these reasons, it is usual to step in and manage the area to prevent these undesirable changes taking place.

Management

One possible form of management would be to graze the plants much more heavily than normal during summer. In Chapter 3 (p. 31) it was pointed out that experiments have shown that when about 60%

of the new growth is removed each year, heather plants remain in a 'juvenile' condition. This means that they continue, year after year, to produce new shoots which have the high nutrient quality typical of young plants. Further, the amount of woody material is not increased and the plants do not grow any taller. This sounds like an excellent way to manage heather, but unfortunately it is seldom, if ever, possible in practice. It requires a high stocking density of grazing animals in summer, and a low density in winter. The problem becomes one of how to feed the animals in winter. This has been partly overcome in various ways – by supplementary feeding or by wintering the animals on other farms or grasslands away from the heaths. But none of these is a complete solution, and stocking densities are invariably restricted by the amount of 'winter keep' available to the farmer. (Stocking densities on heaths vary from 1 sheep to 1·2 ha to 1 to 2·8 ha: these are much lower than on grassland.) This has the effect that, from this viewpoint, heaths are always undergrazed in summer.

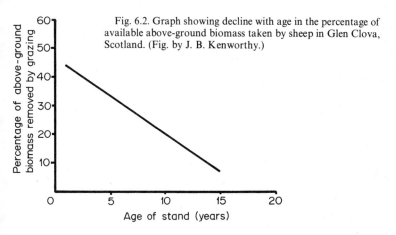

Fig. 6.2. Graph showing decline with age in the percentage of available above-ground biomass taken by sheep in Glen Clova, Scotland. (Fig. by J. B. Kenworthy.)

It is implied in what has been said that although heather provides forage of reasonable nutrient content, heaths can support only a rather low level of herbivore production, the actual amount depending largely on the proportion of young heather in the area. It has been suggested that increased productivity could be achieved by supplying fertiliser to improve the nutrient content of the shoots.

This has been tried. The provision of extra nitrogen in fertiliser

causes increased shoot production in heather and higher concentrations of nitrogen in the edible parts. Phosphatic fertiliser increases
the amounts of phosphorus in the shoots. No doubt this would lead
to the possibility of increased stocking densities. Animals such as
hares, rabbits and grouse can, in fact, recognise and select the shoots
of plants which, as a result of fertiliser treatment, are more nutritious,
just as they recognise and prefer to graze on young plants – though
by what senses they pick out these shoots is not known. Experiments
such as that illustrated in Fig. 6.3 show that the breeding success of
grouse is greater where heather stands have been treated with fertiliser, and leads to larger populations in subsequent years.

Fig. 6.3. Diagram illustrating an experiment on the effect of fertiliser treatment of heather on the population and breeding success of grouse. (From
Miller, Watson and Jenkins, 1970.)

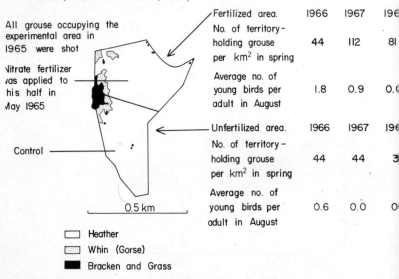

Fertilized area.	1966	1967	196
No. of territory-holding grouse per km^2 in spring	44	112	81
Average no. of young birds per adult in August	1.8	0.9	0.(
Unfertilized area.	1966	1967	196
No. of territory-holding grouse per km^2 in spring	44	44	3
Average no. of young birds per adult in August	0.6	0.0	0

All grouse occupying the experimental area in 1965 were shot

Nitrate fertilizer was applied to this half in May 1965

Control

0.5 km

☐ Heather
▧ Whin (Gorse)
■ Bracken and Grass

Nonetheless, it is not really economic to try to improve the grazing
value of heather by using fertiliser. It is expensive to apply fertilisers
in the generally rather rough terrain of heathlands, and the increase
in production would scarcely be sufficient to warrant this expense.
The effects, particularly in the case of nitrogen, last only a few years.
Finally, some of the effects are wasted when the 'crop' is a perennial,
bushy plant, because some of the increased production goes into
increasing the proportion of wood.

Some other form of management is therefore needed, and from very early times the management 'tool' has been fire (Plate 4a), which prevents the heather plants from progressing to the mature and degenerate phases, when production of new shoots declines and the proportion of wood increases. Although there is an interval of a few years while the stand recovers after burning, it is returned to the productive high-quality 'juvenile' condition each time it is burnt. For the reasons given above, and others to be discussed in Chapter 7, stands should be burnt before the end of the building phase, that is usually before they reach 15 years of age. They can often be burnt effectively by the time they are about 10 years old, and the compromise frequently aimed at is about 12.

Having considered the reasons for the use of heaths as grazing land, and the necessity for management, it remains to examine the ecological effects of grazing.

Herbivore production and nutrient depletion

In Chapter 5 it was suggested that the levels of herbivore production are not sufficiently great to amount to a serious drain on the nutrient fund of a heath. This is borne out in general by the figures in Table 6 for nutrients removed per unit area in wool and sheep carcasses. However, these have to be viewed against the total fund of available nutrients in the system and the amount of any inputs. When this is done it may be concluded that at least in the case of phosphorus, animal produce could lead to significant depletion. It has been argued that because on heathland soils both phosphorus and available nitrogen are often limiting factors, it is inappropriate to take a 'protein crop' (i.e. animal produce) which is bound to be rich in these two elements.

The effects of grazing on the vegetation: deflected successions

On most heathlands it is difficult, if not impossible, to disentangle effects due directly to grazing from those due to burning, for the one factor seldom operates without the other. However, there are some ways in which the influence of the biotic factors may be identified.

During colonisation of bare ground and the subsequent development of vegetation, the first colonists give place to new arrivals as conditions change and communities replace one another in a recognisable sequence. This is plant succession (Chapter 4, p. 48). The ability of any plant to enter the succession depends on the conditions of the habitat, and the alterations in these conditions made by the previous occupants of the habitat. If, during the course of succession, some new environmental factor is introduced, this may so alter the conditions that the course of succession is deflected and plants may enter which otherwise would not have taken part at all.

The entry of grazing animals to an area undergoing succession provides an example of the introduction of a new environmental factor (in this case a biotic factor), and may be expected to cause deflection of the succession. On heathland, every time burning takes place, in the course of recovery of the vegetation a plant succession takes place. Compared to successions on rock, sand or some other surface which has never before carried vegetation, the post-fire succession is rapid because it takes place on a surface which has already matured under a previous plant cover. For this reason it is described as a 'secondary succession', in contrast to 'primary successions' on areas never previously colonised. It is because of this rapid recovery rate that burning is an appropriate form of management of heath vegetation for grazing, and animals often have access while the secondary succession is in progress. There is then an opportunity to demonstrate experimentally some aspects of the influence of grazing animals and to compare the course of succession in the presence of the biotic factor with that in its absence.

In an area which is regenerating after fire, and is open to grazing, a number of sample plots can be fenced to exclude animals, and their development compared with that in a nearby unfenced plot. Under suitable conditions regeneration of heather is rapid in protected plots, sometimes forming a nearly closed stand in as few as two growing seasons.

Where the unfenced plots are subject to very heavy grazing, redevelopment of vegetation is much slower and for several years much of the ground remains bare of cover. In particular, heather and other species of Ericaceae suffer severely if all the newly-grown shoots are repeatedly nibbled off. Because sheep tug as well as bite when grazing, seedlings are often pulled right out of the ground and uneaten parts are seen lying about. Grasses, sedges and rushes are more resistant, and at least for a time may be the major constituents of the developing vegetation.

In this way it may sometimes come about that, after burning, the immediate application of heavy grazing may change the composition of a community from heath to some form of grassland. The competitive vigour of heather is reduced more than that of certain grasses. The particular species of grass concerned depends upon soil conditions: on a moist peat it is frequently mat grass (*Nardus stricta*), on wet hill slopes where water seeps through the soil purple moor-grass (*Molinia caerulea*) may spread, while on the richer, less acid and better drained soils a mixture of brown bent grass (*Agrostis canina*) and sheep's fescue (*Festuca ovina*) may establish a sward.

The first of these is worthless as a pasture plant, and its spread at the expense of heather is a retrograde change as far as productivity is concerned. Purple moor grass is also of limited value, but an *Agrostis–Festuca* pasture can be a positive improvement. On soils capable of carrying *Agrostis–Festuca* therefore, it is good practice to encourage the replacement of heather by grass, by introducing heavy grazing after burning. Sometimes this is more easily achieved by allowing cattle rather than sheep to graze the area, and once the change has been made the grasses gradually bring about improvement of the soil by producing a milder, less acid humus than heather. Eventually the level of herbivore production in the area may be increased by this means alone.

Where, however, soils are poorer it is better to encourage the return of heather and therefore to avoid such heavy grazing during regeneration after a fire. It may be impossible to exclude grazing altogether, though this might be desirable for a few years. However, as explained in Chapter 3, p. 31–33, heather responds rather well to mild grazing and may be encouraged to produce a spreading growth form. This speeds up the development of cover and of a dense stand of heather. Under properly adjusted management, grazing may actually stimulate the production of young shoots in heather to a level above that of normal production in ungrazed plants.

Animals as a cause of vegetational change

Just as the vegetational changes during regeneration after a fire can be deflected by the action of grazing animals ('deflected succession'), so the application of heavy grazing to well-established stands of heather may cause changes. For example, heavy grazing and trampling by cattle can, in the course of a few years, kill out heather and lead to its replacement by grass. Rabbits, too, can destroy heather by heavy grazing, but this influence is usually confined to the immediate neighbourhood of burrows or warrens.

It is difficult to say which is the more damaging, grazing or trampling. Certainly heather is very susceptible to trampling and to the passage of wheeled vehicles, as can be seen in areas frequented by tourists. Experiments have shown that walking up and down in heather only 40 times can kill the trodden branches and create a path.

Even where grazing pressure is insufficient to kill heather, it may be weakened in comparison with other aggressive species. A notable example is bracken which is believed to have spread in heathland areas since the introduction of intensive sheep grazing.

Dependence of grouse on heather

It may seem strange to speak of a bird as a grazing animal, but in fact, after the nestling stage when insects are eaten, grouse (Figs. 5.3, 5.4) are herbivores, depending to a very great extent upon the one food plant. In winter their diet consists almost entirely of heather, and even in summer when other plants are taken as well, heather still accounts for a substantial proportion. It is therefore quite appropriate to regard grouse as a grazing animal, although it never exerts a very heavy grazing pressure. As mentioned on p. 67 grouse are never sufficiently numerous to take more than a small proportion of the available food. There is no evidence of competition for food between grouse and sheep at normal stocking rates, and frequently heathland is used for both.

However, because of its strong dependence upon the one source of food, the relationship between grouse and its food plant is of great ecological interest, and has been the subject of detailed investigations by members of the Mountains and Moorlands Research Station of the Nature Conservancy.

On most grouse moors considerable numbers of birds are shot each autumn, and it might be thought that this would be a chief factor in controlling the population. This is not so, because each year breeding results in a larger number of birds than the area can support. Grouse take up territories in the autumn, and even in the absence of shooting only a limited number of the more aggressive birds can find territories. The rest are surplus birds and tend to move about in flocks during winter. Should any territory-owners die, their places are taken by the surplus birds, but by the time the breeding season comes round in spring many of the surplus birds have died or moved away from the area. The only effect of shooting is to reduce the total population numbers in autumn and there are always sufficient birds at that time of year to fill up the area available for territories.

In spite of this, there are very considerable fluctuations from year to year in the grouse population of a given area of heathland. It has already been suggested that the density of grouse is related to the age of heather (p. 77) and to the nutrient content of the heather shoots (p. 80), so it seems that food plays some part in determining numbers. But if grouse eat only 5% of the available food in an area it is difficult to think of an explanation of how this can be so.

Over a period of years, variations in the size of the grouse population in a study area in north-east Scotland proved to be correlated with the quantity and age of the heather, suggesting some effect of food supply on numbers. However, this was by no means a simple relationship for it turned out that breeding success (the number of young reared per adult bird) varied with the growth of heather in the *previous* summer and the amount of die-back in winter. This seems to affect the nutrient quality of the food available in early spring, and it appears to be quality at this time of year, rather than quantity, which is critical as far as breeding is concerned. Breeding success in one year determines the breeding stock in the following year. The final conclusion is intriguing and of considerable ecological importance: the breeding stock of grouse in any year is dependent to a large extent on the growth of heather during the summer, not of the immediately preceding year, but of the one before that (Fig. 6.4).

One further aspect of the relationship between grouse and heather needs to be mentioned. When grouse shooting first became popular about the middle of the nineteenth century, landowners and game-keepers thought that burning, practised until then for the benefit of sheep, should be reduced or discontinued because grouse required tall heather for cover and nesting. Later a serious decline in grouse populations occurred, reaching disaster populations about 1872–3. An inquiry was set up, and the decline was attributed to a disease caused by a parasitic roundworm. The remedy suggested was to resume burning on the grounds that this might help to control the parasite. To a considerable extent this had the desired effect, but it was a classic example of prescribing the right remedy for the wrong reason.

In fact, the parasite was only the immediate, and not the fundamental, cause of death and declining populations. The real cause was almost certainly the declining nutrient quality of the heather shoots, all over the country, as the stands increased in age in the absence of burning. When burning was resumed, pioneer and building heather again occupied a fair proportion of the total heathland area and grouse populations picked up again. Since that time, the importance of burning management in maintaining good stocks of grouse has been verified experimentally by comparing the numbers of birds

Fig. 6.4. Scheme to show how grouse numbers may be influenced by the condition of heather available 12 months previously (modified from Watson and Miller, 1970).

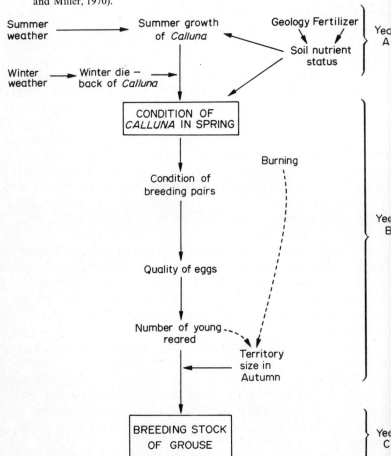

over a period of years on adjacent sites, one of which remains unburnt while a proportion of the other is burnt each year (Fig. 6.5).

It remains true that grouse require a certain amount of older, taller heather in which to nest. Every territory must contain tall (late building or mature) heather. When managing for grouse it is a mistake, therefore, to burn heather in large blocks, although there is less objection to this where sheep are the primary concern. A very large block of young heather will not be fully utilized by grouse because it can accommodate only a restricted number of territories if each is to contain some of the adjacent older heather. It is far more satisfactory to burn numerous small patches or strips (Plate 4d) when, although a large proportion of the total area is occupied by young heather, each patch is adjacent to older stands. This type of management can accommodate the maximum number of terri-

Fig. 6.5. Diagram illustrating an experiment on the effect of heather-burning management on the populations and breeding success of grouse.
Left: Map of the area in 1961 at start of experiment.
Right: Map of the area in 1966 after completion of burning programme. (From Miller, Watson and Jenkins, 1970.)

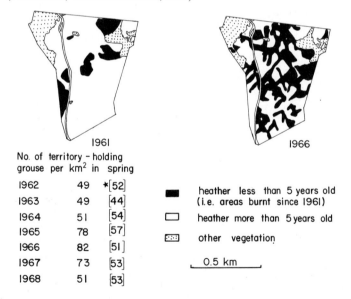

1961

1966

No. of territory - holding
grouse per km² in spring

Year	No.	
1962	49	*[52]
1963	49	[44]
1964	51	[54]
1965	78	[57]
1966	82	[51]
1967	73	[53]
1968	51	[53]

■ heather less than 5 years old (i.e. areas burnt since 1961)

▢ heather more than 5 years old

▦ other vegetation

⊢___ 0.5 km ___⊣

*These figures refer to an adjacent control site of unburnt heather

tories. A widespread survey of Scottish grouse-moors verified that, in general, estates managed on this principle had the higher stocks of grouse (Picozzi, 1968).

Throughout this chapter the essential part played by burning in managing heathland for grazing animals has been evident. In Chapter 7 detailed consideration is given to fire as an environmental factor having important effects upon the whole ecosystem.

Suggestions for practical work

1. In a study area which is grazed by large herbivores such as rabbits, hares or sheep, important information may be obtained by systematic observation of the animals, using binoculars, from a suitable, concealed vantage-point. Observations taken during set periods at different times of day will reveal the daily grazing habits of the animals. If several plant community-types are contained in the visible area, differences may be found in the density of animals (numbers per unit area) on each type, and estimates made of the average time spent grazing there. If observations are repeated at different times of year changes in the pattern of grazing related to season may be revealed.

2. If a heather area is subject to heavy grazing, an estimate of the amount of plant material taken by the grazing animals may be made, using relatively small, movable cages to protect sample areas for short periods of time (not more than one month). The protected areas might be about 1 m^2 or larger, allowing a sample to be cut from $\frac{1}{4} \text{ m}^2$ in the centre – to prevent sampling too close to the netting. Several such cages are required to provide an adequate sample, and the dry weight of the cut heather is compared with that from a similar number of unprotected squares (each taken close to its protected counterpart). Assuming the time interval is short enough for little growth to have taken place outside the cages, the difference in the mean weights per unit area represents the amount removed by grazing. The process can then be repeated for another time interval, after moving the cages to new sites.

3. Where grazing animals play an important part, it is often instructive to follow the changes in the plant community in areas from which they are excluded. A stout wire-netting fence is required – if rabbits or hares are to be excluded, the bottom edge must be buried a good 30–40 cm, and the fence must be high enough to

discourage them from jumping over. It is better to fence several areas rather than just one, to provide comparisons and to separate chance results from those due to the prevention of grazing. Each one should be as large as possible, so as to minimize the influence of the wire-netting on the local environment (e.g. shading, rain-splash, reduction of wind speed, which may have significant effects close to the fence).

Permanent quadrats should be marked out both inside and outside the fenced area and charted at regular intervals. The cover and frequency of all species in the community should be recorded at intervals inside and outside the enclosures, using randomly placed samples. (In a single growing season changes may not be great, but differences in growth and flowering of a number of species may be recorded. Over two or three years marked changes may begin to show.)

4. In some areas, recent changes in grazing intensity may be having important effects on the vegetation, e.g. the introduction of cattle may be causing an increase in the cover of grasses at the expense of heather. Such changes may be examined by periodic analyses of the cover contributed by the most important species, and by detailed recording of permanently marked sample areas.

5. Devise an experiment in the study area to test the effect of nitrogenous fertiliser on the growth of heather (e.g. ammonium nitrate). The level of application could match that used on grass fields on neighbouring farms, and may be compared with stronger and weaker applications and with a control (as an example, in the experiment described in Fig. 6.3, ammonium nitrate was supplied at a level representing $105 \, kg \, ha^{-1}$ of N). Notice carefully whether grazing animals are attracted to fertilised plots.

6. Using tame rabbits, tests may be carried out to show whether there is a preference for heather at any particular growth phase, and to determine the order of preference for the various species of the heath community. A choice is given of weighed quantities of the different food plants, and after a given time the amounts remaining are weighed and the quantities taken calculated. Does the rabbit select in the same way when it is well-fed as it does when it is hungry? Will it take the less palatable foods more readily when preferred ones are not available?

7 Fire

Fire has been used in the management of heathland from the earliest times (Chapter 2). This is because grazing alone was seldom adequate to prevent the progress of succession towards woodland. Probably burning was irregular and rather infrequent to begin with, but became a recognised method of management when extensive sheep-farming was introduced to heathlands (Fig. 7.1). The rather low productivity and rough terrain of most heathlands demanded a cheap but effective management 'tool' which was capable of controlling large areas, using minimum man-power. Shepherds adopted the aim of burning every heather stand, as far as possible, at 10-year intervals. Many heaths must have had a history of regular burning since about 1800, and may have been subject to fire irregularly for a long period before this. Clearly, fire constitutes an ecological factor of major importance.

Objectives of management by burning

Fire achieves, in the course of a single operation, several distinct objectives which may be set out as follows:

(*a*) preventing re-colonisation of heathland by tall shrubs and trees,

(*b*) preventing heather stands reaching the mature or degenerate phase, in which a high proportion of the biomass consists of wood,

(*c*) creating the conditions required for uniform regeneration, leading to even-aged stands having high productivity of edible new shoots (Plate 4c).

The normal, well-controlled fire is expected to remove the greater part of the vegetation, usually leaving only about 15 cm (or sometimes a little more) of charred stems projecting from the ground. Plants of the ground layer including mosses and lichens are usually burnt, and exposed litter may be slightly charred. A properly managed fire does not set the litter or surface humus alight. However, occasionally if a fire gets out of control or is started accidentally it may get excessively hot. The surface humus may then be ignited and fires of this kind may continue to burn, or at least to glow and smoulder, for days or even weeks, until all the surface organic matter is burnt off and the upper mineral soil exposed. However, in routine burning there is little risk of this happening.

The use of fire for these purposes in British heathlands may be compared with its widespread use in vegetation management elsewhere in the world. A case in point is the use of fire in the savanna grasslands of Africa, which are burnt much more frequently than heathlands (usually every year). In general terms the objectives are similar: prevention of shrub and tree colonisation and the stimulation of herbage production for grazing animals.

Regeneration

The suitability of heather for management in this way depends on its capacity for vegetative regeneration – that is to say, the production of clusters of young shoots from the old stem-bases which are not usually killed by the passage of fire. This has been explained in Chapter 3 (p. 32). The normal fire clears away all the above-ground parts of the plants but leaves the stem bases. Buried in the soil surface, humus, litter or carpet of mosses and lichens, there are reserve buds

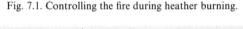

Fig. 7.1. Controlling the fire during heather burning.

which have been protected from all but minor rises of temperature. The young shoots they produce (Plate 4b) are presumably able to draw on a fully developed root system, at least for a while.

A second means of regeneration is the germination of seed and establishment of seedlings. Where conditions are suitable, vegetative regeneration is 'backed up' by seedling establishment, and the seedlings, in spite of slower growth at first, fill in the gaps between the regenerating stem-bases of the former stand of heather plants. Further, it sometimes happens (p. 97) that vegetative regeneration is sparse or fails altogether, and redevelopment of a heather stand then depends entirely on seedling establishment. This may require up to six years or so before full cover is restored, instead of two or three years when vegetative regeneration is vigorous.

After a fire, the resulting habitat is usually favourable for seed germination and seedling development. This is particularly true where the surface is composed largely of organic matter (raw humus or peat) which retains moisture effectively. (Surfaces composed largely of mineral particles are inclined to dry out and this may inhibit germination or cause the death of young seedlings). Heather seeds germinate best where exposed to light and where temperatures fluctuate (p. 23). Both these conditions are satisfied in the bare areas created by fire, which warm up rapidly during the day and frequently cool equally rapidly by radiation from the surface at night.

There is also some suggestion that the fire itself may act as a stimulant to the germination of heather seeds. Experiments have given an indication that the number of seeds germinating and the rate of germination may be increased by short periods of heat treatment, ranging, for example, from 25 seconds at 160 °C to 1 minute at 40–80 °C. These are the temperature levels expected just below the litter or humus surface in a normal fire. To this extent heather may be regarded as fire-adapted, and fire may encourage rapid regeneration from seed.

Ecological effects of fire

Management of any kind affects an ecosystem in various ways. When it takes the form of periodic complete destruction of the above-ground parts of all plants in the community, with repeated redevelopment of a cover of vegetation, the influence must be considerable. Much research has been devoted to discovering the nature of this influence.

Temperature

In assessing the effects of fire it is essential to have some idea of the temperatures reached and their duration, because this determines the impact of burning upon the vegetation and its habitat. Before 1961 there was no information on this point, but in that year Miss E. Whittaker published the results of work in which temperatures reached in heath fires in Scotland had been measured. The method used was to place large numbers of temperature indicators at various levels in the vegetation and soil (canopy level, stem level, ground surface, immediately below surface, etc.) before an area was to be burnt. The indicators were made of small strips of mica (which is unaffected by high temperatures) on which 'thermocolours' were painted in stripes. These are paints which change colour at a specific temperature. A series of different thermocolours can be bought (p. 102), each of which shows a colour change at a different temperature spanning the range 50 °C to 950 °C at intervals of between 20 ° and 50 °C. These are painted on the mica strip in order and the indicator is placed in the pathway of the fire. Afterwards it is collected and the maximum temperature reached is given by the highest member of the series which has changed colour. The value is approximate, but sufficient to give a valuable indication of the temperature reached.

Using these indicators, it was found that at 20 cm above the ground in a heather canopy temperatures between 500 °C and 840 °C were often recorded. At ground level they never rose so high and were usually between 300 °C and 500 °C. The insulating properties of humus or peat and various types of litter or moss carpet were strikingly demonstrated: for example, where the temperature at a peat surface was 400 °C during a fire as little as 1 cm below the surface there was a rise of only 30 °C.

However, this method records only the maximum temperatures reached and not their duration, though it has the advantage of ease and cheapness. Large numbers of indicators can be placed in an area about to be burnt, so giving an idea of the pattern of variation in temperatures reached. To find out how long these temperatures are sustained requires more elaborate apparatus – thermocouples are placed among the plants and the leads, extending to recording apparatus at a safe distance, are buried before the fire is started. Continuous recording of the changing temperatures of the thermocouples is obtained, using a battery-driven recording potentiometer.

By this method, Miss Whittaker's results have been confirmed by other workers and it has been shown that the high temperatures last usually only from $\frac{1}{2}$ to 1 minute, while the time from the beginning of heating to return to normal is not more than 2 to $2\frac{1}{2}$ minutes.

This is because the fire usually passes fairly quickly through the vegetation. The rate varies considerably according to weather conditions, particularly wind speed. The actual temperature produced in the fire is determined by a number of factors including wind speed, rate of passage, and the amount of moisture in the vegetation and soil. Under some conditions very hot fires result, with temperatures rising to nearly 950 °C, while at the other extreme 'cool' fires may produce only 250 °C to 350 °C in the canopy. In the latter, not all the available fuel in the vegetation is burnt up and varying proportions of the stems and branches and of the moss or lichen layer may be left behind.

Thermocouple measurements also revealed another very important factor which controls the maximum temperatures reached. If weather conditions etc. remain constant, temperature is directly related to the age of the stand – the older the stand, the hotter the fire (Fig. 7.2). This follows from the fact that the older the stand, the greater the proportion of wood, and so the greater the amount of fuel available.

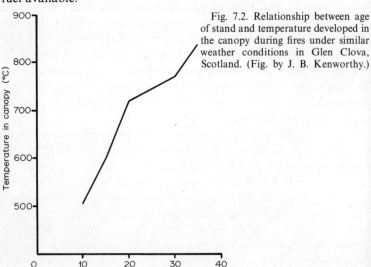

Fig. 7.2. Relationship between age of stand and temperature developed in the canopy during fires under similar weather conditions in Glen Clova, Scotland. (Fig. by J. B. Kenworthy.)

Effects of fire: smoke and ash

The immediate consequences of a fire are that most of the above-ground parts of the vegetation disappear. There are vigorous flames, a great deal of smoke (Plate 4a), and a layer of ash is deposited on the ground. Most of the carbon contained in the vegetation is released as carbon dioxide, and the smoke (which consists of particles and gases) also contains a large quantity of nitrogen and some other substances such as sulphur. Often about 70–80% of the total nitrogen contained in the vegetation disappears in smoke, and 50% of the sulphur. The exact amount depends on the temperature of the fire and at temperatures above about 400 °C significant quantities of other nutrients such as potassium may be lost in smoke, while the same applies to phosphorus at about 800 °C.

Ash

The remainder of the nutrient elements contained in the vegetation are deposited on the ground in the form of ash. It has long been known that some substances are readily dissolved from ash by water, and the suspicion arose that after a fire a proportion of the nutrient fund might be lost to the heath ecosystem as a result of being dissolved in rainwater soaking the ash and draining through to the lower soil levels, passing eventually into streams and rivers. Some preliminary experiments seemed to confirm this. Blocks of soil with their vegetation in position were cut from heath stands and placed in special containers. The vegetation was burnt and the ash allowed to fall on the soil surface. Water was then sprinkled on in amounts equivalent to natural rainfall, allowed to drain through, and collected from the base of the containers. Analysis of this water indicated that as much as 2·5% of the total fund of nutrients (the fund contained in vegetation *and* soil) might be lost in this way.

In Chapter 6 it was mentioned that, in the past, a ten-year burning rotation has often been adopted as an aim. Assuming regular burning has been going on for 200 years, this might mean that a single heather stand could have been burnt 20 times. To allow for failure to achieve this frequency of burning, we may halve this figure and say ten times. Then if each time 2·5% of the total fund of nutrient elements were lost, the rather alarming conclusion is reached that in 200 years 25% or $\frac{1}{4}$ of the total nutrients might be lost as a result of this system of management.

A suggestion of this type, made about 1953, led to greatly in-creased research and discussion on this subject. It was pointed out that account had not been taken of inputs of nutrients to the eco-system during the period of years between fires. From Chapter 5, p. 70, it can be seen that, in a country such as Britain situated close to the sea, there are inputs in rainfall which, over the period of years between fires, would be significant. A comparison, such as that made by Chapman (1967) for a Dorset heath, suggests that for most nutrients the amount arriving in the interval between fires is more than sufficient to make up for the loss during a fire (Table 7). This, however, may not be the case for phosphorus because the amount contained in rainfall is very small. On the other hand the loss of phosphorus by solution from ash is also not large because this element is deposited in a rather insoluble form. But in this con-nection it is worth remembering that animal produce involves a relatively sizeable drain on the phosphorus fund (Chapter 6, p. 81). Nitrogen is another element for which, in some studies, losses exceed inputs in rainfall, because losses (in smoke, particularly) are high. In this case, however, it is difficult to generalise because the input amounts seem to vary from one part of the country to another. It should be added that the argument put forward in this paragraph rests on the assumption that a large proportion, at least, of the nutrient input in rainfall is retained in the rooting region of the soil. This has not yet been fully verified.

TABLE 7

Comparison of nutrients lost in smoke during heathland burning in Dorset, with input from rainfall over a 12-year period between fires.
$kg\ ha^{-1}$

	Na	K	Ca	Mg	P	N
Loss of nutrients in smoke	1·5	8·3	12·5	4·0	2·2	173·1
12 years' input in rainfall	305	14	56	67	0·12	62
Gain (+) or loss(−)	+303·5	+5·7	+43·5	+63	−2·08	−111·1

(Data from Chapman, 1967)

The conclusion arising from these studies seems to be that, after all, burning management does not have the serious effects on soil fertility that at one time seemed possible. However, although this effect of fire on the habitat can now be seen in proper perspective, it is not possible to generalise and it may be that burning has played some part in causing the phosphorus deficiencies which characterise most heathland soils.

Rules for proper use of fire for heathland management

Arising from the experiments and observations which have been summarised, a set of general rules can be drawn up which should govern the use of fire as a management 'tool', in order to minimise any damaging ecological effects.

First, weather and other conditions should be judged so that, while an effective fire is obtained, temperatures should not exceed about 500 °C in the canopy. If this is adhered to, temperatures at ground level will not exceed 400 °C. There is reason to believe that if this limit is much exceeded the stem-base is killed and vegetative regeneration prevented.

Second, stands should be burnt before they pass out of the building phase. It is difficult to lay down any exact age, as this will vary according to habitat. It has often been said that burning should, in any case, take place before the plants exceed 15 years of age and this seems to be borne out on ecological grounds. There are several reasons:

(a) Because by this time productivity of young shoots per unit area has reached its peak and a proportion of production each year is going into wood.

(b) Because stands exceeding 15 years of age usually produce temperatures well above 500 °C in the canopy (p. 94). Not only does this often prevent vegetative regeneration (see above), but it also causes excessive loss of nutrients in smoke (p. 95).

(c) There is a steady decline in the success of vegetative regeneration as stands increase in age, particularly after about 15 years. One explanation is that as the stands become progressively older a self-thinning process takes place. Many of the original main stems die off because the foliage they bear is shaded by that of neighbouring branches. This means that there are fewer stem-bases per unit area when it comes to regeneration after a fire.

(d) There is continual accumulation of litter on the ground which tends to hold a proportion of the nutrient fund out of circulation. Regular burning keeps litter accumulation to a minimum.

(e) The heather is becoming tall, and should be burnt before it much exceeds 30 cm.

Third, burning should take place in small strips or patches, not normally exceeding about 2 ha (Plate 4d). Burning of very large blocks should, wherever possible, be avoided (see pp. 87 and 101).

Fourth, burning should not be too frequent: in most habitats intervals should not be less than ten years. More frequent burning results in returning too often to bare ground or to the conditions associated with pioneer heather, introducing risks of loss by erosion and the spread of unwanted plants. It might also cause unnecessary nutrient loss if the interval between fires becomes too short for inputs to exceed losses.

Burning is restricted by law to a certain period of the year. In Scotland this period begins on October 1st and ends on April 15th (with some extensions, by permission, in wet years when the weather has interfered with burning). In England the dates are slightly different (November 1st to March 31st). Weather conditions usually further limit the time available for burning to the months of October (in Scotland), February (in some years), March and (in Scotland) early April. Most burning is traditionally carried out in spring, but there is some evidence that regeneration is rather better following autumn burning.

Other ecological effects of fire

Plant species vary greatly in their capacity to withstand the effects of fire. Generally speaking, those with underground organs of perennation or vegetative propagation can survive the destruction of their aerial parts and produce new growth from below. Those lacking structures of this type and depending upon reinvasion of the area by seed are more readily eliminated from the community by burning, unless they are capable of rapidly establishing large populations of seedlings. This is why burning, even at intervals as long as 10–12 years, normally prevents recolonisation by shrubs and trees. (Juniper is an example of a shrub which, in the absence of burning, would probably be much more widespread than it is in British heaths.)

The properties of heather which enable it to survive burning management have already been discussed. Other species which reappear quickly after a heath fire include bell-heather which germinates rapidly to produce a dense crop of seedlings, and a number of plants which have underground rhizomes or other stem structures, such as cross-leaved heath, blaeberry, crowberry and bracken. Some of the grasses and sedges have a densely tufted or tussock habit and even if the surface of this is burnt many of the growing points are unaffected: these include moor mat-grass, purple moor grass and 'deer grass'* (*Trichophorum caespitosum*). In fact, a number of these plants are less affected by the passage of fire than heather and reappear more quickly. For a time they may become the most prominent members of the community, and heather only re-establishes its dominance later on because of its greater competitive ability. In this way, a succession takes place as indicated on p. 82.

Secondary successions following burning

The secondary successions after heath fires vary according to the rate of regrowth of the plants which survive the fire. Sometimes this regrowth is so rapid as to establish nearly 100% cover before any colonisation of the exposed raw humus or peat can occur. Generally, however, at least in patches, there is a stage of colonisation of the bare ground by gelatinous green algae (*Cystococcus, Zygogonium*) and lichens (e.g. *Lecidia uliginosa*). The species concerned and the rate of their spread depend on the amount of moisture in the surface, but their greatest development takes place in one or two seasons after burning.

On soils with a well-developed upper horizon of organic material, the next stage is usually one of a mixture of lichens of the genus *Cladonia*, and mosses, at first mainly species of *Polytrichum*. On more mineral soils a variety of grasses and flowering plants may gain entry at this stage – for example bent grass (*Agrostis tenuis* and *A. canina*), sheep's fescue (*Festuca ovina*), common milkwort (*Polygala serpyllifolia*), common speedwell (*Veronica officinalis*), common violet (*Viola riviniana*).

While these changes are taking place, species of the original community are regenerating. On rather well-drained soil, bell-heather often quickly establishes dominance by the rapid development of numerous seedlings. Elsewhere there may be temporary phases of dominance by wavy hair-grass, blaeberry or crowberry. However,

*This English name is given in quotation marks to draw attention to the fact that the plant is not a grass but a sedge.

in most cases heather is steadily regenerating and sooner or later its growth outstrips the rest both in height and in lateral spread, and after a number of years (from 2 to 10), it again becomes dominant.

Monoculture of heather

The aim of burning, and its inevitable result, is to lead as quickly as possible to the re-establishment of a uniform, even-aged stand of heather in the building phase (Plate 4c). In this condition the stand is dense and its canopy is smooth, even and continuous, allowing little light to penetrate. Heather in this growth-phase is at the height of its competitiveness, and excludes all but a few other species. Rather weak plants of bell-heather and tormentil (*Potentilla erecta*) may survive here and there, and there may be small patches of mosses such as *Hypnum cupressiforme* or *Dicranum scoparium*, or the lichen *Cladonia arbuscula*, but little else. Effectively this is a monoculture, and the diversity of the accompanying flora is very much reduced. The same is true in general of the invertebrate fauna.

There is an implication of the monoculture of heather which is of great ecological importance. It has already been said that heather litter is acid and slow to decompose. The humic acids it produces mobilise iron and aluminium oxides, which, in the company of some of the nutrient elements, enter into solution in rainfall draining through the soil. This process of leaching depletes the 'A' horizons of these elements, and although they may be redeposited at a lower level in the soil they are effectively removed from the rooting region of the vegetation. Heather, therefore, encourages soil podsolization which is generally regarded as a process of deterioration. Further, in heathland soils iron deposition in the 'B' horizon often leads to the formation of a hard iron pan (pp. 10–11). This may become impermeable to the passage of water, leading eventually to waterlogging of the upper layers of the soil and a change towards bog vegetation.

In so far as fire maintains a monoculture of heather, it leads indirectly to further soil podsolization. This indirect effect may be of greater consequence ecologically than the direct effects of nutrient loss in smoke or by the leaching of ash.

Possible consequences of mis-use of fire

Burning may lead to undesirable consequences if, for any reason, re-establishment of vegetation is delayed and the bare soil surface is exposed for too long a time. Loss of particles from the surface may

deplete the nutrient fund, and plants which are worthless to herbivores may spread, notably bracken and moor mat grass. Application
of burning under conditions which are likely to produce this type of
result represent mis-use of fire. Examples include burning when
weather conditions are likely to produce too hot a fire, and burning
when heather is too old – though sometimes the latter cannot be
avoided. In both cases, subsequent regeneration must be largely
from seed and this may be slow.

As explained earlier in this chapter, too frequent burning is also
a mis-use of fire. So is burning at high altitudes and in high rainfall
districts. Fire is still widely used in the wet, western parts of Britain
where heather is less vigorous. On wet, peaty soils it may fail to
recover after burning, permitting the spread of 'deer grass'. Where
recolonisation is slow, peat surfaces are particularly liable to erosion.

Burning, especially if frequent, may also be misguided if carried
out on very steep hillsides. Here, whether or not conditions are
suitable for quick regeneration, erosion may occur while the surface
is exposed. It may take the form either of sheet erosion, when
particles of humus are removed as rainwater runs off the surface, or
gulley erosion when deep channels are cut into the soil and their
contents spread out in a fan at the foot of the slope. Upland Britain
is not often thought of as a region where erosion is a serious problem, but many hillsides show mild or severe symptoms. Often a clue
to the result of years of depletion of surface humus is the number of
visible boulders or the extent of scree on a hillside which would
otherwise be heather-covered (Fig. 7.3 overleaf).

All these results of the mis-application of fire are intensified
wherever, as so often, sheep have access to the area during the course
of regeneration. They are attracted to the new growth (p. 77) and
delay the development of cover. This extends the time during which
particles may be removed from the bare area.

It remains true that if heather is to be managed inexpensively to
provide grazing for herbivores, burning is the way to do it. Much
more is known now than even 20 years ago about the ecological
effects of fire on the heathland ecosystem and it seems that, under
appropriate conditions, it can continue to be used without serious
damage to the habitat. The rules are clearly understood and if they
are obeyed the aims of management are realised. To disobey them
can at times be disastrous.

Suggestions for practical work

1. If part of the study area is managed by burning, try to arrange to be present when this is done. If possible the site should be visited beforehand, all the species listed and their relative cover recorded. The age of the heather should be determined (see Chapter 4, p. 50, no. 4). Make up some temperature indicators as described on p. 93 using thermocolour paints (which may be obtained from SAS Scientific Chemicals, Ltd., Victoria House, Vernon Place, London WC1B 4DR). These are painted on thin mica strips, and in each case a second strip is placed over the painted surface of the first to keep it free from direct contact with burning plants. The two strips are wired together so that the paint stripes comprise the middle layer of a sandwich. A number of these indicators can be made up and set out before the fire in various positions in the vegetation. During the fire notes should be made on the rate of passage of the flames. Finally, collect in the indicators and record the temperatures reached.

2. If possible, the recolonization succession following burning should be investigated over a period of years. Permanent marked

Fig. 7.3. Erosion, probably due to excessive burning on a steep hill slope. Numerous bare patches of rock and stones are visible, the heather cover with its accumulated soil having been lost.

quadrats should be charted annually, and the cover and frequency of all species recorded in random samples (see Chapter 4, p. 50, no. 3). In the years immediately following the fire, samples of the surface humus should be examined microscopically to see if there is a stage in which gelatinous algae or lichens develop, and note should be taken of the entry of mosses and larger lichens. As vascular plants (including heather) begin to appear, determine whether they have developed from seed or vegetatively from underground parts which have not been damaged by the fire (or both).

3. Where there is no opportunity for direct study of recolonization after burning, the main outlines may be reconstructed if a number of stands of different age (since burning) are available. Here again cover and frequency of the various species may be recorded for each stand. Then show graphically the changes in the contribution made by each species (or group of plants, e.g. mosses, lichens) to the community with the passage of time after the fire, and also changes in the total number of species present.

4. Using the ideas given above, compare the recolonization process following fire in areas previously occupied by building-phase heather (e.g. 10–12 years old) with that in areas previously occupied by mature or degenerate heather (e.g. over 15 years old).

5. Using maximum and minimum thermometers and wet and dry bulb thermometers, all suitably shielded from direct sunlight, compare the temperature and humidity close to ground level on a burnt area, with those in a neighbouring heath community. Surface soil samples might also be taken to compare moisture content. Measurements should be made at different times of the day, under various weather conditions, and at different seasons of the year.

6. Investigate vegetative regeneration in potted plants of heather and other heath plants after burning off most of the above-ground parts. (Use a small painter's flame-gun, or even a Bunsen burner if carefully handled.) The temperatures reached can be monitored using thermocouples.

7. If sufficient analytical apparatus is available, it is interesting to determine the amount of elements such as K, Ca, P, which can be extracted by water from the ash deposited after burning. Collect heather from a known area of a dense stand, burn it carefully and collect the ash. Extract with known volumes of water

and measure the amounts of these elements obtained (for methods, see Jackson, 1958). Extracts made from fresh heather plants, or from heather litter, may be compared. If the extract is then filtered through a column of peat, humus, mineral soil or sand and the filtrate again analysed, an estimate may be gained of the efficiency of these substances in retaining the nutrients which may be dissolved out of the ash.

8. Look for signs of erosion in the study area. If these are found, to what cause or causes can they be attributed?

8 Land use and conservation: ecological considerations

In the past rather little attention has been paid to the ecological effects of different types of land use and the management practices they involve. It has been one of the aims of this book to show, in the case of heathland, how some of these effects can be revealed by research. Does this knowledge enable us to make sound choices between various possible types of land use? A choice may be regarded as 'sound' if the result is satisfactory from the standpoint of conservation – taken here in its broadest sense to mean the careful husbandry of natural resources. Defined in this way, conservation aims at a combination of productivity with the ecological health of the system, and although it embraces the protection of wild life this is not its sole concern. With increasing information about the functioning of heathland ecosystems, summarised in the previous chapters, it should be possible to assess the trends of change which result from present types of land use and to set out principles and guide lines for the future.

In fact the future of heathlands is uncertain. In northern Britain, where heaths still occupy wide areas and make an important contribution to the landscape, they have been a subject of controversy, open to the rival claims of hill farming, sport and afforestation. Elsewhere, for example in Sweden, Denmark and southern England, they have been rapidly disappearing during the past 60–100 years, giving place generally to forest or cultivated land. Only a few remnants are left.

Although not highly productive, heathland has survived in upland Britain because it yielded some revenue to the landowner. Hill sheep, and to some extent cattle, retain an important place in the agricultural economy, although heavily supported by Government subsidy. The income from this traditional form of land use is now supplemented by extremely valuable receipts from the letting of shooting rights, without which much of our heathland might have been abandoned long ago, or converted to some other use.

As suggested in earlier pages, it can be argued that some aspects of traditional heathland management are inclined to lead to deterioration of the habitats. The question arises as to whether management of heathland for the production of herbivores can be justified ecologically. If not, can any improvements be introduced to permit the continuation of this form of land use without further damage? Failing this, the alternatives seem to be first, that the land goes out of production, or second, that some entirely different form of land use, such as forestry, might prove more satisfactory. Either way, much of the heathland would then disappear, as it has in many other countries.

This suggests that the future may see some further reduction in the area of heath in Britain. However, quite apart from their agricultural or sporting value, heathlands are important in other respects which are much more difficult to quantify. As already mentioned, they create incomparable scenery which constitutes a tourist attraction, and they provide valuable open space for recreation. In addition their wildlife is distinctive and attractive, and their ecosystems are of great scientific and educational significance. These ecosystems are of particular interest because, although they owe their origin and maintenance to man, they are not intensively managed like cultivated land.

Their vegetation is composed entirely of naturally-occurring plants and their fauna largely of naturally-occurring animals. The landscape is man-made, but rather than making it any less worthy of preservation than a completely 'natural' ecosystem, this gives it an added historical interest.

For all these reasons it is of the utmost importance that a substantial proportion of our heathlands should be protected, some of it in nature reserves. This is the more restricted, though none the less essential, aspect of conservation. If, however, examples of heathland are to be preserved for historical, amenity and scientific reasons, it will not be enough to see that they are left relatively undisturbed. Earlier chapters have indicated the successional changes that would result from this policy, leading to disappearance of the very communities which were of greatest interest. As in so many other cases, conservation here implies positive management, which must be based on ecological principles.

Further consideration is now given to the various possibilities which have been outlined above for the future use of heathlands.

Improvements without major ecological change

Because grouse shooting brings in much needed income on upland estates, it is likely to continue as a major form of land use. Whether or not it figures as prominently in the future as in the past, it seems likely that sizeable areas will be retained as heath for this purpose. Burning will remain the only effective form of management, in view of the fact that it maintains heather stands in a productive condition at low cost, whether the ground is smooth or rough.

Research on the effects of burning, however, has shown (Chapter 7) that, although not likely to cause severe nutrient depletion (as was once thought), it may contribute to deficiencies in certain elements. Even more important may be the indirect effects of heather mono-culture on the soil. If this is true, should this type of management continue in its present form? Although some ecologists are inclined to answer that it should not, it has to be admitted that, at the present time, overall changes in the habitat and vegetation due to burning management must be very slow. The situation is certainly one of low fertility, but the greatest deterioration probably took place long ago in the period immediately following the initial forest clearance. Management for grouse, while not bringing any improvement, probably causes little further deterioration, so long as the rules for proper control of fire are strictly observed.

Attempts have been made to eliminate the need for burning by substituting some means of cutting heather. In experiments, vegetative regeneration has been shown to be better after cutting than after burning. However, there are serious practical difficulties. Because machines are needed this method is not applicable to very rough country, and there is also a difficulty over the disposal of the cut branches. If these are removed, there is an unacceptable loss of nutrients while, if they are left, shading interferes with the growth of new shoots from the stem-bases. No effective substitute for burning has been found.

Positive improvement of the habitat can be achieved by spreading fertiliser, for example by aircraft, and here and there this has been done. On the whole there has not been sufficient return to justify the expense, and it is unlikely that this will become a widespread practice. The only feasible improvement which can be made in management for grouse is to ensure that the burning programme is planned to avoid, so far as possible, all undesirable consequences.

Many of these conclusions apply also to hill sheep farming, where it continues to be practised without major changes in the vegetation. The possibilities for improvement in productivity are very limited, particularly where only one type of grazing animal is concerned. A combination of sheep with cattle, however, can lead not only to an increase in animal produce but sometimes also improvement in the composition of the herbage. The reason for this lies in a marked difference in the grazing habits of the two animals. Sheep are strongly selective, grazing hard on the more palatable plants (particularly certain grasses and heather), whereas cattle discriminate less and take more fibrous material. By themselves, sheep 'punish' the more nutritious plants, allowing unwanted species to spread, but a balanced stocking of sheep and cattle exerts a more uniform influence on the vegetation, keeping the coarser plants in check.

'Reclamation' for agriculture or forestry

Any major improvements of heathland for grazing purposes require the replacement of at least some of the heather-dominated areas by grass. Whereas heather occupies acid, nutrient-poor soils characterised by raw humus at the surface, the more nutritious grasses such as the bent grasses and sheep's fescue occur naturally on the richer, brown soils containing mild humus. Hill grazings which include some of each type of soil can support more stock than those where heathland predominates. Where both are represented, animals graze the heath areas only $\frac{1}{3}$ to $\frac{1}{5}$ as intensively as the grass areas.

This means that in areas which are exclusively, or almost exclusively, heath, considerable improvement can be brought about by converting even quite small patches into grassland. As explained in Chapter 6, on the rather better soils this can be done by intensive grazing alone, especially grazing by cattle (when heather is quite quickly killed by eating and trampling, and its place taken by grass). In most heaths, however, it is necessary to clear an area – usually by burning – and to apply fertiliser and grass seed. Where cultivation of the ground is possible the result is better.

'Reseeding' is usually confined to the more accessible parts of a grazing, and to well-drained land with the best available soil. Once the grass sward has been formed it is grazed intensively and, in the absence of any control, this in time weakens the grasses and permits the return of heather and other heath plants. In the meantime, however, the herbivores have benefited. Also, by the deposition of urine and faeces on surrounding land following grazing of the reseeded area, some of the increased fertility is spread beyond the limits of the improved patch.

More permanent improvement can be achieved only when reseeding is accompanied by control of grazing. This involves fencing, and greatly increases the expense. However, where the necessary money has been available quite spectacular improvements of the quality of a large portion of a hill farm have been made. The conclusion is that the technical and ecological knowledge necessary for substantial improvements of this kind is available. Hill sheep farming has, up to the present, involved ecological deterioration to the extent that it has been described as '200 years of mismanagement of the uplands'. This, however, does not necessarily mean that it could not be continued on a more satisfactory basis if certain changes were to be introduced. These however require an input of money. Traditionally hill farming has been a marginal type of farming carried out by tenants, crofters or other small-holders with little or no capital at their disposal. Any major change would require a radical alteration of this system.

Forestry has been hailed as a type of land use which not only produces a commercially rewarding crop from heathland, but also brings about positive improvements to the habitat. These claims deserve examination.

On the credit side, the following points can be made:

(a) Modern forestry involves deep ploughing even on steep slopes or rough, bouldery ground. This destroys the podsol, breaking up an iron pan if present, and raising part of the 'B' horizon of the soil (where nutrients leached out of the upper layers have been deposited) to the surface. All this improves the availability of nutrients to the plant roots.

(b) The widespread use of spruce, largely a consequence of its good growth and productivity, means that a deep-rooting tree is introduced, which will tend to increase the cycling of nutrients in the ecosystem.

(c) Fertilisers are applied at the time of planting and, as required, later – so increasing the phosphorus, nitrogen and, if necessary, the potassium status of the soil.

(d) A sizeable plantation may create sufficient shelter to improve the local climate of the area.

But there are also points to be listed on the debit side:

(*a*) A plantation, for much of its life, is a dense even-aged stand of trees which does not encourage diversity of wild life. Many plants are excluded by the shade cast, and animal and bird life may be restricted. (Nonetheless conifer plantations are probably more appropriate in the northern and upland parts of Britain where heath is widespread, than they are in some other parts of the country. As they get older and more mature, and the canopy is reduced by thinning, plants and animals formerly characteristic of the native pinewoods may be encouraged: examples are the red squirrel, pine marten, crested tit and capercaillie.)

(*b*) Conifer plantations contribute litter to the soil surface which forms an acid raw humus much as heather does. After the initial disturbance of the soil, podsolization processes are resumed under conifers. The result does not necessarily amount to soil improvement.

(*c*) The final timber crop represents a removal of nutrients from the ecosystem. How this affects the balance sheet on a former heathland is still to be fully investigated, bearing in mind the input from fertilisers in the early stages. However, wood consists largely of lignin, which is a type of carbohydrate compound. There is, therefore, little drain on nitrogen and phosphorus, the two elements which are available in least quantity in the soil.

It is not easy to weigh up the pros and cons. At least forestry is a productive form of land use which involves inputs as well as a harvest, and so is not exclusively exploitive in its operation. Its apparent success, however, must be attributed in part to the fact that it has large-scale financial backing, whether in the form of a Government enterprise (the Forestry Commission), or of large private estates. Without this, little headway could be made, for forestry involves heavy capital investment over a long period before any return is received.

In general, it seems likely that the area of heathland used for forestry, already large, will increase, and in all probability this will represent an ecological gain. Certainly productivity from other forms of land use is low or negligible on many heaths, which could profitably be used for forestry.

Retention of heathland for amenity and wild life conservation

To some extent the interests of grouse shooting will ensure the retention of considerable areas of heathland. This may also serve to preserve typical heath landscapes, and the continuation of the open country which is so attractive for recreational purposes. (Only during the relatively short shooting season, from August 12th to the end of autumn, is public access restricted.)

Unfortunately, however, management for grouse (or, for that matter, for sheep) does not also serve the purpose of conservation of heathland wild life. One reason, though not the most important, is that in the interests of grouse certain predators are still, occasionally, needlessly destroyed – for example wild cat and birds of prey, such as the buzzard, hen harrier or golden eagle. (Just as there are ample surplus grouse each year to take the place of those which are shot, so this surplus can generally make good any loss due to predators. Grouse populations are not controlled by predators.) The more important reason why management for herbivores is incompatible with the aims of nature conservation is to be found in the objectives of burning. The chief purpose of burning (p. 100) is to keep as much of the area as possible covered by uniform, even-aged stands of building heather. In this phase heather is most vigorous and dense, excludes all but a few other plants, and creates conditions to which only a restricted range of animal species is adapted.

By contrast, wild life conservation aims at developing the maximum diversity of plants and animals of which a particular ecosystem is capable. To achieve this in heathland requires an uneven-aged stand of heather in which plants are allowed to complete their natural sequence of growth-phases, leading to interruption of the canopy by gaps forming as bushes become degenerate and die out (Plate 3d). Variation is introduced into the habitats (p. 42) and the community is enriched by numerous plants which the more varied conditions can support. The vegetation becomes a patchwork instead of being uniform and crop-like, and this patchiness emphasises the differences in micro-habitat. This in turn leads to a greatly increased diversity of animal life, populations of many different species basing themselves side by side where local conditions are appropriate.

It follows that management in a heathland nature reserve must reduce burning to a minimum, or eliminate it altogether. Some means must be found, however, to prevent the inevitable scrub and tree colonisation. If this cannot be done by hand an occasional fire may be necessary, but areas should if possible be kept free from burning for 40 or 50 years at a time.

There is also a problem as to what is an adequate size for a heathland nature reserve. No general answer can be given, because different plants and animals require different areas for the maintenance of viable populations. An interesting study was carried out on the heaths of Dorset by N. W. Moore (1962). At one time heathland in this county was extensive, but it has been broken up progressively into smaller and smaller fragments. For a number of characteristic plants and animals of Dorset heath communities it is possible to find a minimum area below which they disappear – this is particularly evident where the fragments of heath are isolated from others and cannot readily be recolonised, for example after a fire (Fig. 8.1). Among the animals which were absent from the smaller and more isolated heaths were certain dragonflies and moths, the sand lizard and the Dartford warbler.

Fig. 8.1. Map of Dorset heaths showing the effects of isolation on the distribution of eight animal species characteristic of heathland, four of which are confined to heathland habitats (the silver-studded blue butterfly, a dragonfly, the sand lizard and the Dartford warbler), while four are found in other habitats as well (another dragonfly, the grayling butterfly, the viviparous lizard and the stonechat). Figures at arrows give the number of indicator species observed in the area designated: the upper figure shows the number out of the four confined to heathland, the lower figure gives the number out of the four which occur also in other habitats.

The more isolated fragments of heath contain fewer of these species, particularly those confined to heathland. (From: Moore, 1962.)

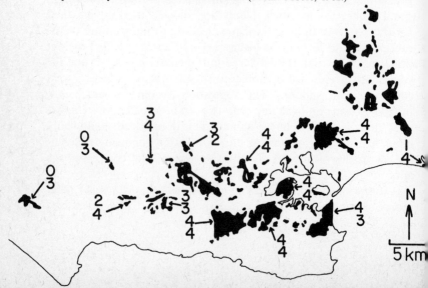

There is also a good argument for allowing some examples of heathland to develop naturally without any form of management. Sooner or later shrubs or trees gain access, usually in groups which form clumps or thickets. In the course of time a canopy is formed which locally excludes heath plants. A common tree colonist is the birch (Fig. 8.2). The clumps, thickets or small birch woods which can result when heather is colonised develop a grassy vegetation in the place of heather. Birch, being a broad-leaved deciduous tree, deposits abundant leaf-litter and the humus derived from the leaves is of the mild type. This is readily decomposed and nutrient cycling is enhanced, with consequent soil improvement.

Patches of birch wood add greatly to the attractiveness of the landscape, and introduce a further element of diversity into the flora and fauna. From the viewpoint of nature conservation they are highly desirable, though they have no commercial value. Even in a heathland area which is used for grazing or sport, a case could be made for allowing certain parts to develop for a time into birchwood. Later, the areas could be returned to grazing land, probably in better condition after a period under the influence of birch trees and their grassy ground-flora.

Fig. 8.2. Colonisation of heathland by birch wood (with a few Scots pine trees) when management is discontinued (N.E. Scotland).

These examples draw attention to a point of view now widely accepted in regard to nature conservation. This is that it is desirable to aim for diversity – diversity in the habitat and diversity in the plant and animal communities. In the case of the management of heathland reserves, diversity can be attained through the natural sequence of growth-phases of heather; in the uplands in general, diversity is introduced by adopting a variety of forms of land use rather than concentrating on one alone, and by allowing certain areas to follow the course of succession to woodland without interference. In both cases the result is a greater variety of wild life in a region than where habitats or vegetation are uniform. At the same time, there is probably less risk of disturbance if one component of an ecosystem should suffer change – perhaps due to some exceptional climatic extreme or other accidental event. Where diversity and variety exist this change can be absorbed by adjustment on the part of other plants and animals, but where uniformity prevails the loss of one important member may be disastrous.

Throughout this book emphasis has been placed on the study of heathland as a functioning ecosystem, and as an ecosystem which has been produced and maintained by man. The management practices he adopts have been treated as factors of the environment and their influence upon the habitat, vegetation and fauna have been examined. The results of this work open up the possibility of making an ecological assessment of a traditional form of land use. In the light of this, alternative types of land use can be subjected to a similar scrutiny. Ecology is a branch of biological science, but in this context it can be applied to practical problems. In the long run decisions on various types of land use and management will be made on economic and sociological grounds, but they will be ill-founded decisions if they fail to take the ecological assessments into account and to pay due attention to scientific research such as that described in this book.

Suggestions for practical work

1. Make a map showing land use in the vicinity of your study area, paying particular attention to areas which were formerly heathland but are now forest, grassland, cultivated land, etc. Gather as much information as you can to compare the productivity of these areas with that of the heathland.
2. As a result of all your practical work, can you draw up any guide

  lines for improvement of the management of the heathland
  study area?

3. If possible, carry out a small-scale experiment to see how easy
   or difficult it is to convert the heath to grassland. From a given
   area, cut off the existing vegetation. Give the surface a shallow
   cultivation and sow an ordinary agricultural grass-clover mixture. Record the success with which the sown species establish.
   Compare the fate of part of the area which is left untouched with
   another part in which you imitate grazing by using a pair of
   shears. Further information can be gained by using fertiliser on
   part of the area, with another part left untreated as a control.

4. Where heathland has been claimed for forestry or for grassland,
   find out what treatment the land has received. Can you assess
   whether or not the habitat has been effectively improved? How
   will its productivity compare with the remaining heathland?
   What has been lost in terms of wild life, scenery, etc.? Try to
   draw up a balance sheet of advantages and disadvantages.

5. For the heathland study area, draw up a report assessing its
   importance as a wild life habitat. Consider carefully the criteria
   you adopt and finally decide whether the area merits recognition
   as a Site of Special Scientific Interest or a Nature Reserve.

6. Supposing the study area is to be managed as a Nature Reserve,
   draw up a management plan, basing it on the information you
   have gathered about the area. The plan should aim to maintain
   or improve the existing range of habitats and diversity of fauna
   and flora, and should ensure the survival of scarce or specially
   interesting species.

Appendix

In many places where peat cutting has occurred, vertical exposed faces of peat can be found. Careful examination of the freshly cut surface shows various bands of material, some blackish in colour while others are dark or light brown. In most peats, these bands contain the remains or partial remains of plants. The macroscopic remains in peat range from whole plants in the case of *Sphagnum* moss in the upper layers of the peat to, lower down, the blackened remains of heather twigs, the silver bark of birch trees, large pieces of the red wood of pine, and in the lowest layers, leaves of rushes and sedges together with shining undecomposed seeds of the bog bean. From these remains we can visualise the changes in vegetation which have occurred in this one area over a period of several thousand years. However this is only a very limited sample of the changes in the past and if we wish to get a more general picture of changes in the flora we must look more closely at the peat.

Peat has been forming slowly since the glaciers began to retreat more than ten thousand years ago and throughout this period a slow rain of pollen has landed. The pollen was then permanently preserved in the acid and anaerobic surface of the peat. We can look at such a record in a very simple and effective way. The basic idea is to separate the pollen grains from a known volume of peat, to examine the different types of pollen which occur and in this way describe changes in vegetation.

While looking at a peat profile in the field small samples of each peat type, or peat at a variety of depths, can be taken and transferred to the laboratory for closer examination. A fresh vertical surface is cut to avoid any possible contamination from present day pollen.

From this clean face individual samples are removed with a sharp knife or trowel and placed in a specimen tube.

In the laboratory the sample is removed from its tube and two sub-samples of 1 cm^3 are taken. Precise volumes can be obtained by placing two razor blades 1·0 cm apart in a small block of wood and using this device to cut a sample $1 \times 1 \times 1$ cm. It is preferable to collect at least two sub-samples from each depth in the peat. Place each sub-sample in a conical flask with 20 ml 5% NaOH or KOH. (Pre-drying the sample and crushing in a pestle and mortar gives a much better recovery of pollen, but fresh samples can be used for general examination.)

Fig. A.1. Diagrams of five types of pollen grain commonly found in peat. (Fig. by J. B. Kenworthy.)

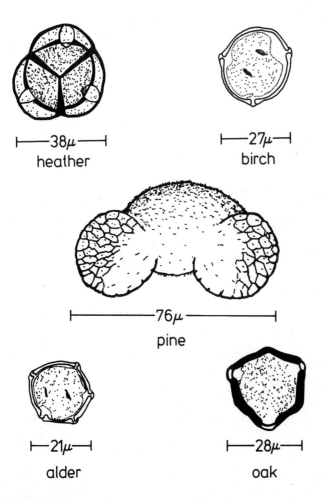

This mixture is simmered for ten minutes and any large fragments of peat are broken down with a glass rod. The hot mixture is passed through a 0·2 mm sieve (or two layers of fine muslin will do) to remove large debris. The filtrate is placed in a centrifuge at low speed (approximately 1 500 r.p.m. for five minutes).

The supernatant liquid is carefully decanted, leaving a small pellet of fine particles and pollen grains at the bottom of the tube. At this point add more water to the pellet in the centrifuge tube, shake up the pellet and recentrifuge to obtain a washed pellet.

This pellet is then made up to 2 ml with distilled water, or distilled water and a few drops of safranin or basic fuchsin, the solution is stirred and four drops are examined on a slide under a cover slip. The individual pollen grains are counted from a total of 20 microscope fields at a magnification of × 100.

Very useful information can be obtained by simply comparing the number of pollen grains from tree species with other types. With a little practice it is possible to recognise a number of the main pollen types and in this way to get a fairly good estimate of the proportions of tree, heath and herbaceous pollen. A reference collection of pollen types requires only a little effort and the differences in structure between such species as pine, oak, birch, and heather are quite apparent. However to go much further than general identification leads one into a very specialised field.

Five easily distinguished pollen types are shown in Fig. A1.

References and suggestions for further reading

List A   Further reading

A fuller and more detailed treatment of heathland ecology is given in
GIMINGHAM, C. H., 1972. *Ecology of Heathlands*, Chapman and Hall.

The following are suggested sources of additional information and ideas:
BURNETT, J. H., (editor) 1964. *The Vegetation of Scotland,* Oliver and Boyd.
FRASER DARLING, F. and MORTON BOYD, J., 1964. *The Highlands and Islands,*
   Collins.
GIMINGHAM, C. H., 1960. Biological Flora of the British Isles. *Calluna vulgaris*
   (L.) Hull. *J. Ecol., 48,* 455–83.
MCVEAN, D. and LOCKIE, J. D., 1969. *Ecology and land use in upland Scotland,*
   Edinburgh University Press.
PEARSALL, W. H., 1950. *Mountains and Moorlands,* Collins.
TANSLEY, A. G., 1939. *The British Islands and their Vegetation,* Cambridge
   University Press.

Recommended for further details of methods of soil analysis:
JACKSON, M. L., 1958. *Soil chemical analysis,* Constable.

List B   References cited in the text, together with a small selection of other papers relating to specific topics

ALLEN, S. E., 1964. Chemical aspects of heather burning. *J. appl. Ecol., 1,*
   347–67.
BARCLAY-ESTRUP, P. and GIMINGHAM, C. H., 1969. The description and
   interpretation of cyclical processes in a heath community. I. Vegetational
   change in relation to the *Calluna* cycle. *J. Ecol., 57,* 737–58
BARCLAY-ESTRUP, P., 1970. The description and interpretation of cyclical
   processes in a heath community. II. Changes in biomass and shoot
   production during the *Calluna* cycle. *J. Ecol., 58,* 243–9.
BARCLAY-ESTRUP, P., 1971. The description and interpretation of cyclical
   processes in a heath community. III. Microclimate in relation to the
   Calluna cycle. *J. Ecol., 59,* 143–66.
BEIJERINCK, W., 1940. *Calluna*: a monograph on the Scotch heather. *Verh.
   Akad. Wet. Amst.,* (3rd Sect.), *38,* 1–180.
CHAPMAN, S. B., 1967. Nutrient budgets for a dry heath ecosystem in the south
   of England. *J. Ecol., 55,* 677–89.

CRISP, D. T., 1966. Input and output of minerals for an area of Pennine moorland: the importance of precipitation, drainage, peat erosion and animals. *J. appl. Ecol., 3*, 327–48.

DIMBLEBY, G. W., 1962. The development of British heathlands and their soils. *Oxf. For. Mem., 23*,1–121.

DURNO, S. E., 1965. Pollen analytical evidence of 'landnam' from two Scottish sites. *Trans. Bot. Soc. Edinb., 40*, 13–9.

FITZPATRICK, E. A., 1974. *An Introduction to Soil Science*. Oliver and Boyd.

FORREST, G. I., 1971. Structure and production of North Pennine blanket bog vegetation. *J. Ecol., 59*, 453–79.

FREELAND, P. W., 1970. The productivity of the Scots Heather (*Calluna vulgaris*) in the *Calluna-Ulex minor* complex of Ashdown Forest, Sussex. *J. biol. Educ., 4*, 297–304.

GIMINGHAM, C. H. and MILLER, G. R., 1968. Measurement of the primary production of dwarf shrub heaths. In: *Methods for the measurement of primary production of grassland*. I.B.P. Handbook No. 6 (Ed. C. Milner and R. E. Hughes). Blackwell Scientific Publications.

KAYLL, A. J., 1966. Some characteristics of heath fires in north-east Scotland. *J. appl. Ecol., 3*, 29–40.

KENWORTHY, J. B., 1963. Temperatures in heather burning. *Nature, 200,* 1226.

MILLER, G. R., 1964. The management of heather moors. In: Symposium on land use in the Scottish Highlands. *Advmt. Sci., 21,* 163–9.

MILLER, G. R., WATSON, A. and JENKINS, D. J., 1970. Responses of red grouse populations to experimental improvement of their food. In: *Animal populations in relation to their food resources*. Brit. Ecol. Soc. Symposium No. 10 (Ed. A. Watson). Blackwell Scientific Publications.

MOORE, N. W., 1962. The heaths of Dorset and their conservation. *J. Ecol., 50,* 369–91.

PICOZZI, N., 1968. Grouse bags in relation to the management and geology of heather moors. *J. appl. Ecol., 5,* 483–8.

ROBERTSON, R. A. and DAVIES, G. E., 1965. Quantities of plant nutrients in heather ecosystems. *J. appl. Ecol., 2,* 211–19.

WATSON, A., MILLER, G. R. and GREEN, F. H. W., 1966. Winter browning of Heather (*Calluna vulgaris*) and other moorland plants. *Trans. Bot. Soc. Edinb., 40,* 195–203.

WATSON, A. and MILLER, G. R., 1970. *Grouse management*. The Game Conservancy, Booklet 12. Fordingbridge, Hampshire.

WATT, A. S., 1955. Bracken versus heather, a study in plant sociology. *J. Ecol., 43,* 490–506.

WHITTAKER, E., 1961. Temperatures in heath fires. *J. Ecol., 49,* 709–15.

(The abbreviations of Journal titles used in the above list are those authorized in the 'World List of Scientific Periodicals' which can be consulted in many libraries.)

Index